Ride with the Sun

". . . How soon may I ride this whole world about?"

"You must rise with the sun, and ride with the same
Until the next morning he riseth aflame;
And then Your Grace needs not make any doubt
But in twenty-four hours you'll ride it about."

King John and the Abbot of Canterbury
Old English Ballad

Ride with the Sun

An Anthology of Folk Tales and Stories from the United Nations

EDITED BY

HAROLD COURLANDER

for THE UNITED NATIONS WOMEN'S GUILD

Illustrated by Roger Duvoisin

WHITTLESEY HOUSE

McGraw-Hill Book Company, Inc.

NEW YORK   TORONTO   LONDON

Published by Whittlesey House
A division of the McGraw-Hill Book Company, Inc.
Printed in the United States of America

THE UNITED NATIONS WOMEN'S GUILD

This book has been compiled by the United Nations Women's Guild, an independent association of women connected with the United Nations Secretariat or with national delegations. Founded in 1948, the Guild counts among its members women from many countries and from all continents. In addition to fostering a sense of community among these different nationalities, it has as its objective the support of voluntary humanitarian and relief work anywhere in the world where need is felt.

Devoted principally to the relief of distress among children, Guild members have made thousands of garments and arranged for their distribution. The Guild has sponsored schools and orphanages, and whenever natural disaster such as flood or hurricane has occurred, it has been prompt to respond with clothing, food, money and services.

Guild members have also assisted UNICEF and UNESCO in important fund-raising campaigns for the alleviation of distress in many areas.

All royalties derived from the sale of this book will be devoted to similar humanitarian work.

ACKNOWLEDGMENTS

The United Nations Women's Guild gratefully acknowledges the assistance received from the delegations to the United Nations concerning the selection and editing of the stories in this book; and extends its thanks also for the general cooperation of the Department of Public Information.

It is impossible to name the many people whose help in the collection of stories, in typing, in translating, and in clerical work has been so freely given, but to Guild members and their friends, to officials of permanent delegations and members of the Secretariat of the United Nations who have contributed help, the book committee is sincerely grateful.

Particular thanks are extended to all authors and publishers who have granted free permission for the use of already published stories, the sources of which are listed in the editorial notes on pages 283–296.

Among the many who have helped in obtaining material, the following deserve a special word of appreciation:

The Ministry of Education, Bogotá, Colombia, and the Transvaal Education Department, Pretoria, South Africa, for the stories from their respective countries.

Mrs. Ellen M. Hopkins (Ellen Moore), R.N., Director of the Samuel Grimes Maternal and Child Welfare Center, Kakata, Liberia, for the Liberian tale.

Señora Maria Concepción Leyes de Chaves, President of the Inter-American Commission for Women, Pan-American Union, Washington, D.C., for the legend from Paraguay.

Mr. Ulric Williams of Wellington, New Zealand, for his help in procuring source material for the Maori story, MAUI THE FIRE-BRINGER.

Dr. A. P. Elkin, University of Sydney, Australia, for his suggestions and advice in procuring Australian aboriginal materials.

Dr. Harry Tschopik, American Museum of Natural History, New York, for his suggestions and help in procuring the Bolivian story, THE COMING OF ASIN.

Dr. James A. Notopoulos, Trinity College, Hartford, Connecticut, for his help in securing the Greek story, THE SON OF THE HUNTER.

*This book is dedicated
to the world's needy children.*

The Children's Charter

There shall be peace on earth; but not until
Each child shall daily eat his fill;
Go warmly clad against the winter wind
And learn his lessons with a tranquil mind.

And thus released from hunger, fear and need,
Regardless of his color, race or creed,
Look upwards, smiling to the skies,
His faith in man reflected in his eyes.

CONTENTS

THE PACIFIC

EASTERN AND SOUTH ASIA

ASIAN AND AFRICAN MIDDLE EAST

9

AFRICA

EUROPE

THE PACIFIC

MAUI THE FIRE-BRINGER
[*New Zealand—A Maori Tale*]

Some lands lie above the water, and some below. It was the hero Maui who brought Te-ika-a-maui, or New Zealand, to the surface where it lies today. It was Maui who invented the barb for the fish spear. It was Maui who invented the trap door for the eel pot. It was Maui who invented the kite. It was Maui who brought man the knowledge of how to make fire. And it was Maui who made the days long enough for man to do his work. Many, many things Maui did for the people.

When Maui was born he was small and misshapen, and his mother abandoned him in the wilderness by the edge of the sea. But he was cared for by the sea gods and taught wisdom by his ancestor in the sky, Tama-nui-ki-te-rangi. And when he was old enough he returned to the earth to find his family. When he arrived, he saw his brothers playing spear-throwing games. They saw the misshapen boy and laughed. But Maui called out his name and said he was their youngest brother. They refused to believe him. His mother came and said, "You are not my child." Maui replied, "Didn't you desert me in the wilderness by the edge of the sea?" In sorrow for her deed, and in gladness that Maui had come back, she said, "Yes, I had forgotten. You are my child."

Maui stayed with his people then. And when his brothers went fishing in their canoe Maui said, "I will go too. Am I not the younger brother?" But they would not take him. They said, "No, we do not need you." They went without Maui, but their luck wasn't good, for their fish spears had no barbs on them. Having learned great wisdom from Tama-nui-ki-te-rangi, his ancestor in the sky, Maui showed his brothers how to put barbs on their spears so that the fish wouldn't fall off. And when they went eel-fishing their luck wasn't good, for the eels that swam into the traps escaped by the same door they had entered. So Maui invented a trap door for the eel pots, and when the eels entered they could not get out. But the brothers resented Maui and refused to take him in their canoe.

One day Maui hid in the bottom of the canoe and covered himself with the footboards. When the brothers were out at sea, one of them said to the others, "How good it is not to have Maui with us here." From under the footboards Maui called out, "But Maui is here!" And he removed the footboards which covered him and came out. The brothers looked toward the shore, and they saw it was too far to take Maui back. But they wouldn't give him a hook to fish with.

Maui wasn't angry. From under his belt he brought out a magic fish hook, made from the jawbone of an ancient ancestor. But they wouldn't give him bait to put on his hook. So Maui struck his nose and made the blood run. He smeared blood on his hook and lowered it into the water where it was deep. His brothers caught no fish, and they thought Maui would catch no fish. But he let his line out, and the hook went down to the bottom of the sea. "Why are you stubborn?" his brothers asked. "There are no fish here. Let us go elsewhere." Maui only laughed and waited. Then there was a powerful tug on the line, and the canoe trembled. Maui held the line firmly. His brothers took hold and helped him. Slowly, slowly, the monster of the deep came upward. And when it reached the surface, Maui's brothers cried out with awe and terror, for it covered the water further than the eye could see. This great creature was Te-ika-a-maui, the Fish-that-Maui-caught —the island of New Zealand. The brothers leaped upon its back to cut off meat, but the fish struggled. Where they cut with their knives there came to be ravines; and where the fish's skin became wrinkled as it threshed around, mountains were formed. Thus did New Zealand appear from the bottom of the waters and remain to be the home of the Maoris.

As time passed, Maui noticed that the days were too short, for Tamanuitera, the sun, moved across the sky so rapidly that people didn't have time to dry their *tapa* cloth or to gather their food. Tamanuitera came up, soared across the sky and set, without regard for the needs of man. Maui resolved to make the sun slow down.

"Let us tie the sun and make him go slower, so that the people have time to do their work," he said to his brothers.

But his brothers said, "No, it can't be done, for the sun will burn all those who come too close."

Maui answered, "You have seen the things I can do. Have I not raised the great land of Te-ika-a-maui from the bottom of the water? I can do even greater things."

In this way, Maui persuaded his brothers. He took hair

from the head of their sister Hina. He took green flax. And out of these things he had his brothers plait ropes. Out of the wisdom given him by his ancestor in the sky, Maui gave magical powers to the ropes. Then they made a net, and when it was finished they began their journey to the edge of the world where the sun first appeared each day. Many months passed before they reached the edge of the world. They came to it in the darkness of night, and placed their net over the opening from which the sun would come out.

In the morning Tamanuitera came through and found himself tangled in the great net. He struggled. The brothers held the net and threw other ropes around the sun and tied them. The sun thrashed from side to side as he felt the nooses grow tight. He grasped the ropes in his hands and tried to tear them apart, but they were too strong. Then Maui took his magic war club, made of the jawbone of his ancient ancestor, and went forward and began to beat the sun with it. The sun fought back with a mighty burst of heat, which drove the brothers away, but Maui stood his ground and fought. They struggled back and forth, until the sun cried out, "I am the mighty Tamanuitera! Why do you beat me?"

"Because you rush across the skies so swiftly that people don't have time to gather their food. They are hungry," Maui said.

"I don't have time to spare," Tamanuitera said.

They fought again, and at last, wounded and weakened, the sun cried, "Stop! I will move slowly!" He gave his word, and so they released him from the net.

Tamanuitera kept his promise. Since that day he has moved slowly, and now the people have time to dry their *tapa* cloth and gather their food. But some of the ropes that Maui put on him remain. They can be seen sometimes as bright beams of light piercing through the clouds.

These great things Maui did. Still, the people did not know how to make fire. Maui decided to get this knowledge from the underworld. He went down through a hole in the earth and found Mafuike, the female guardian of fire. He asked her for an ember. She gave him one of her burning fingernails, and he started away. But when he was out of her sight, he said, "This is fire, but people need the knowledge of how to make it." So he put out the flame in a running stream and went back for another ember. Mafuike gave him another flaming fingernail, and he returned to the stream and extinguished it. Again he went to the fire deity, and again she gave him a flaming fingernail. Nine times he went, and nine times he threw the fire into the water. When he appeared for the tenth time and asked for her last flaming fingernail, Mafuike flew into a great rage over Maui's mischief. She chased him out of the underworld, but Maui was so swift she couldn't catch him. He taunted her as he ran, and in violent anger she took her tenth flaming fingernail and threw it at him. It set the grass and the forests on fire, and Maui fled before the onrushing flames. The fire threatened to destroy everything. In great distress Maui called on the rain to help him, and it fell, halting the vast conflagration. Seeing that the world's last fire was being

18

extinguished, Mafuike picked up bits of fire here and there and hid them in the trees.

Since that day, fire has remained in the world, hidden where Mafuike put it. But man knows now how to bring it forth, simply by the rubbing of one kind of wood on another.

THE IGUANA'S POISON BAG
[*Australia*]

In former times, when the earth was young, things were different among the animals than they are today. In those ancient times Ooyu-bu-lui, the black snake, had no poison, but Mungoon-gali, the great iguana, did.

It is said that Mungoon-gali was larger then than now, and that he was a terror to the people of the country. He would go here and there, recklessly killing people with his poisonous bite, and he was feared everywhere.

At last all the animal tribes held a great meeting at the water hole to see what could be done to halt the iguana in his endless slaughter of human beings. There was a great deal of talking, with some creatures proposing this and others proposing that, but they couldn't devise a plan to save their human brothers from Mungoon-gali. So the meeting began to break up in failure. But just at that moment Ooyu-bu-lui the black snake came and asked what the talking was about.

Dinevan, the emu, told him that the iguana was so merciless toward human beings that the human tribe was in danger of being exterminated unless something were done about it.

Bohra, the kangaroo, said: "Even if we went to fight with him, he would kill us with the poison he carries in his hidden bag. Though we don't want our relatives, the human beings, killed, we don't know how to stop Mungoon-gali."

Ooyu-bu-lui the black snake said, "It is I who will save the people from the iguana."

They asked him, "How will you do it?"

And he replied, "That is my secret. But the sun will not go down to rest tomorrow before I shall have taken Mungoon-gali's poison bag away from him."

They listened and said, "Then the sun will not go down before you lie dead from Mungoon-gali's poison. Whoever fights Mungoon-gali dies."

"Did I speak of fighting?" the black snake answered. "Is there no way to gain victory but by fighting? Let those who fight die. I shall not fight, I shall live, and I shall get the poison bag. I do not fear Mungoon-gali."

Ooyu-bu-lui the black snake went away from the meeting, thinking about how he would gain victory over the iguana. He knew he would have to be shrewd and cunning, for the iguana was bigger and stronger, he was quicker of hearing and of movement, and, above all, he had the poison bag. The black snake decided to wait until the iguana was gorged with food.

So he went near Mungoon-gali's camp and lay down to sleep. In the morning when the light came, the black snake watched the iguana come out of his camp, and at a safe distance he followed him. He watched the iguana attack three men and kill them with his poisonous bite, and he watched while the iguana ate his victims. Then the iguana went back to his own camp. He now was drowsy from his big meal, and lay down and went to sleep.

"This is my chance," Ooyu-bu-lui said to himself, creeping forward silently. He raised his club to strike Mungoon-gali, but then he hesitated, saying to himself, "First I must find out where he keeps his bag of poison and how he uses it. If I had it I would be the most powerful and feared of all creatures."

So instead of striking the iguana, the black snake waited. Mungoon-gali slept restlessly. At last he awoke, sat up, and saw Ooyu-bu-lui. He rushed forward to attack Ooyu-bu-lui, but the black snake cried, "Wait! If you kill me you will not hear what I have come to tell you. There is a plot against your life."

"I fear no plot," the iguana said. "What can the tribes do against me? Haven't I killed so many men that they are afraid? And aren't the animal tribes afraid?"

"As long as you know their plans, you need not fear them," the black snake answered. "But if you don't know what is in their minds, you are in danger."

"Tell me then," Mungoon-gali said.

"This is what I had intended to do," Ooyu-bu-lui replied. "But you were going to kill me even though I hadn't harmed you. So why should I speak to save your life?"

The iguana said, "Tell me of the plot, and I will spare your life and the life of your tribe forever."

"Ah, you promise," the black snake said, "but how do I know you will keep your word?"

"Ask whatever you please, and I will convince you," the iguana told him.

"Very well. While I tell you of the plot against your life, give me your poison bag to hold. Only in this way will I feel safe. And I will tell you what was said when all the tribes met at the water hole to plan your destruction."

"What you ask is too much. Name some other thing," the iguana said.

"That is the way it is with you," the black snake said. "I come to save your life. And you ask me what I want so that I'll feel safe while I do it. And then you refuse. Keep the poison bag, then, and I'll keep my story."

And he moved as though to go away, but the iguana called out, "Stop a moment! Make some other condition."

"No, only this way will I feel secure."

So at last the iguana took the poison bag from where it was hidden in his mouth and put it on the ground close beside him, saying: "Here it is, but do not touch it. It is too strong for you. It will kill you."

"I don't fear it; put it in my hand," the black snake said. "Otherwise I will go."

"Don't go! Here it is," the iguana said. And he handed the black snake the poison bag. "Now tell me of the plot."

"Here is the plot," the black snake said, putting the poison bag in his own mouth. "One of us was to get the poison bag from you and take away your power to harm men. It was I who swore to do it before the sun went to rest today. I could not do it by strength, for you are the stronger. But I brought cunning with me, and by cunning I have gotten the poison. And now I must go to tell all the tribes."

Before Mungoon-gali realized what was happening, Ooyu-bu-lui was gone. Mungoon-gali pursued him, but he had eaten much and he was heavy and he couldn't catch the black snake.

Ooyu-bu-lui came to the water hole where the tribes of

the emu, the kangaroo, the opossum, and the others were gathered. He told them what he had done. They praised him and said, "Now give us the poison bag so that we may destroy it."

But the black snake answered, "Why should I give it to you? It is I who took it. Therefore I shall keep it."

They said, "If you don't give it to us, you shall never live in our camps."

Ooyu-bu-lui replied, "I shall come to your camps as I please."

They said, "Then we shall kill you. You are not big and terrible like Mungoon-gali."

He replied, "You forget the poison bag. It is now I who own it. Whoever interferes with me, surely he shall die."

They realized he spoke the truth, and they didn't try to stop him as he turned and went away.

Ever since that day Ooyu-bu-lui the black snake has had the poison bag, and his bite has brought death. And since that time Mungoon-gali the iguana has been without the poison that once made him the terror of the land, and he no longer can harm men by his bite. And now men avoid the black snake instead of the iguana. But Mungoon-gali has never given up hope of getting the poison bag back, and whenever he meets Ooyu-bu-lui they fight. Though the black snake has the poison, he is unable to kill the iguana with it, because Mungoon-gali is a great medicine man, and he knows the secret antidote which saves him from death. Should he be bitten by the black snake he goes to a certain plant and eats it, and thus makes the poison powerless. This secret is the property of the iguana tribe.

THE TURTLE AND THE MONKEY
SHARE A TREE
[*The Philippines*]

One day the turtle was sunning himself at the edge of the water, and he saw an object floating down river in his direction. When the object came closer, the turtle saw that it was a banana tree. He leaped into the water and swam out to the tree and pulled it to the shore. But he wasn't strong enough to carry it up on solid ground, so he went and found the monkey and brought him back to see the prize.

"Here is a banana tree I saved from the river," the turtle said. "Help me carry it to my farm, and I will plant it."

But the monkey was looking out for himself. He said, "If I do that, I deserve a share of the tree."

The turtle replied, "Help me, and I'll share with you."

So the monkey and the turtle together dragged the tree to the turtle's garden. The turtle said, "Now we will dig a hole to plant the tree."

But the monkey said, "Oh no, we said we would share."

"That is true," the turtle replied. "We'll plant the tree and when it gives bananas each of us will take half."

"Oh no, that's not the way to share," the monkey argued. "We'll divide now. You take half of the tree and I'll take half of the tree."

"It's a poor way to share a tree," the turtle replied.

"Nevertheless, I want my share now," the monkey said. So, reluctantly, the turtle cut the tree in half.

The monkey looked at the top half, with all the green leaves, and as it appeared to be the best portion he declared: "The top half is mine."

So he took the half of the tree with the green leaves away to his own garden and planted it. The turtle planted his part of the tree and pressed the earth firmly all around it. The monkey's green half of the tree soon withered and died. But the turtle's half, which had the roots, grew new leaves, and in a matter of time there were bananas on it.

When the bananas were ripe the turtle wanted to pick them, but he couldn't climb. So again he brought the monkey and asked him to go up and throw the bananas down, saying, "For your efforts I will give you some of the bananas."

The monkey climbed. He sat in the top of the tree and tasted the bananas. The turtle stood waiting, but the monkey didn't throw the bananas down. He sat there eating them.

"Throw me some. I'll catch them," the turtle said.

"Never!" the monkey replied. "You cheated me before by giving me the bad part of the tree and now I am going to eat."

"Throw me a few," the turtle said.

"Here are the skins," the monkey said, throwing banana skins on the ground.

Now the turtle became angry. He went and gathered spines and thorns from the bushes and scattered them around at the foot of the tree; then he hid. When the monkey had eaten the last banana he jumped down and landed on the thorns. He danced around and shouted in pain. Wherever he stepped there were sharp points under his feet.

At last the turtle couldn't keep from laughing at the sight. When the monkey heard him, he ran forward and seized the turtle and turned him over so that he lay on his back. The turtle was helpless.

The monkey then announced, "Now you will be punished for your crimes! Shall I beat you with sticks? Or shall I put you in my mortar and grind you like flour? Or shall I throw you from the top of a mountain?" And he made many other suggestions of this kind.

The turtle said at last: "Yes, it would be nice of you to do this. Throw me from a mountain or pound me in your mortar or beat me with sticks. Anything will be satisfactory, as long as you don't throw me into the water."

When the monkey heard this, he was delighted.

"Ah," he said, "the water! Why didn't I think of it before? I'll finish you off in the water!"

So he picked the turtle up, carried him to the river, and threw him where the water was deepest. There was a splash, and the turtle sank from sight. The monkey was very pleased with himself. Then the turtle came to the surface and poked his head out. He said to the monkey, "Thank you, friend, thank you! Didn't you know that the water is my home?"

KANTCHIL'S LIME PIT
[*Indonesia*]

Kantchil the mouse deer was passing the house which belonged to Farmer. He peeped in the door and saw a fresh banana cake, wrapped in banana leaves. Kantchil was greatly tempted. As Farmer and his wife were away working in the rice fields, Kantchil went in and took the cake. He began to nibble. He went into the field. He opened the leaves a little and ate. As he ate he walked. He opened the leaves wider and wider and stuck his head in further and further. And suddenly because he couldn't see where he was going he fell into Farmer's lime pit.

He was very surprised to find himself there. The pit was very deep. Kantchil was a great jumper, but he couldn't jump out of the lime pit. Finally he sat down to think. As he thought, absent-mindedly he held the almost empty banana leaf in front of him.

"Tuhan, Tuhan!" he said. "God, God!"

As he spoke, Babi the boar looked over the edge of the pit.

"Who says the name of God down there?" the boar asked.

Kantchil was looking into the open banana leaf. He moved his eyes from side to side as though he were reading.

"Hear, hear!" he read. "Tuhan has said it! Today is doomsday! Those who wish to survive should take refuge in the holy cave!"

"Who says today is doomsday?" Babi asked.

28

"Can't you hear what one reads from the holy book?" Kantchil asked petulantly. And he went on: "On such and such a day, which is today, the world shall come to an end, and only those who stand in the sacred lime pit shall be preserved!"

"Is it really so?" Babi asked.

"Do you question the word of Tuhan the Creator?" Kantchil asked sternly.

"No, no! I shall come into the pit with you!"

"Alas," Kantchil the mouse deer said, "it may not be. Only the clean may come here."

"I am clean."

"No, you are always sneezing. It is not permitted to sneeze in a holy place."

"I will not sneeze, I swear!"

"It says here in the words of Tuhan," Kantchil read from the banana leaf, "that he who sneezes must not be allowed to contaminate a holy place and must be thrown out."

"I will not sneeze; I am coming down," the boar said. And he came down.

Kantchil went on reading.

Matjan the tiger looked over the edge of the pit.

"Who says the name of Tuhan down there?" he asked.

"It is doomsday!" the boar answered. "Kantchil reads it from the holy book!"

"Why do you hide there?" the tiger asked.

And Kantchil read: "Only those who reside in the holy cave will not be destroyed!"

"That's why we are here," the boar said.

"Ah, I will join you!" the tiger said.

"No, no, you will contaminate this sacred place!" the boar said. "You are always sneezing!"

Kantchil read from his banana leaf: "He who sneezes in the holy place must be thrown out!"

"I will not sneeze," the tiger said, and he came down.

Kantchil went on reading. Gadja the elephant looked down.

"Who reads the holy words of Tuhan?" he asked. "And why do you sit in the lime pit?"

"Today is doomsday," the tiger and the boar replied, "and we who sit in the holy place will be saved."

"I will join you," the elephant said.

"No, no, you are too big, and you always sneeze!" they said. "You sneeze very much and very loud, and even a little sneeze will defile this holy place!"

"I will not sneeze. I am coming," the elephant said. And he jumped into the lime pit.

They sat together in the lime pit, while Kantchil moved his eyes across the banana leaf.

Suddenly he looked at Gadja the elephant.

"Get out!" he said. "You look as though you are going to sneeze!"

"I am not going to sneeze!" Gadja said. "See, I stand on my trunk so that I won't sneeze!" And he stood on his trunk.

Kantchil went on reading.

Then he looked suddenly at Matjan the tiger, saying, "What did I hear?"

"I didn't sneeze. I merely sniffed," Matjan said.

A dreamy look came into Kantchil's eyes. He suddenly clutched at his nose.

"No, no! May it not be!" he cried. He struggled. And then it came: "A-tchee!"

"He has done it!" the other animals shouted. "He has defiled the holy place! He has flouted the words of Tuhan!"

And all together, in great anger, they took hold of Kantchil and threw him out of the lime pit.

EASTERN

AND

SOUTH ASIA

WHY THE PARROT REPEATS
MAN'S WORDS
[*Thailand*]

In ancient times it was not the parrot which was kept in the house by man and taught to speak, but the lorikeet. For people had found that this small bird was a very intelligent creature, and he needed very little teaching. If he heard a word he could repeat it easily. Not only that, he often spoke his own thoughts to man instead of merely imitating the sounds he heard around him.

But it happened one time that all this changed.

One day, it is said, a farmer saw a buffalo wandering in his rice field. It was his neighbor's animal, but the farmer took the buffalo, killed it, cut up the meat, cooked some and ate it, and the remainder he hid. Part of the meat the man hid on the top of the rice house. The rest he hid in the rice bin.

The next day the neighbor came looking for his animal, saying to the farmer, "Have you seen my lost buffalo?"

The farmer replied, "No, I have seen no lost buffalo."

But just then the farmer's lorikeet spoke up. "My master killed it. He ate some and hid some. Part he hid in the rice bin and part he hid over the rice house."

When the neighbor heard this, he looked in the places the bird had mentioned, and there he found the buffalo meat.

But the farmer said, "Yes, this is where I always keep meat. But I did not see your buffalo. This is the meat of another animal."

The lorikeet called out again: "He killed it. Part he hid in the rice bin and part he hid over the rice house."

The neighbor was perplexed. He didn't know whether to accept the word of the man or the bird. And so he took the matter to court. The trial was set for the following day.

The farmer who had stolen the meat said to himself, "Why should the word of a lorikeet be taken, rather than my word?"

That night he took the bird from its cage and placed it in a large brass pot. He covered the pot with a cloth, so that it was dark inside. Outside, the night was clear and bright. The moon was full. But inside the pot, the lorikeet could see nothing of this. The man began to beat on the pot, softly at first, then more loudly, until it sounded like thunder. He took a dipper of water, dripping a little of it on the cloth now and then so that it sounded like rain. All night long he pounded on the pot and dripped water, and he stopped only when dawn came. Then he took the lorikeet and put it back in its cage.

When it was time for the trial, the farmer took his bird and went to court. The neighbor who had lost the buffalo told how the lorikeet had instructed him where to find the stolen meat. The judge asked the lorikeet for his testimony. The bird repeated what he had said before:

"He killed the buffalo. Part he hid in the rice bin and part he hid over the rice house."

The man who had stolen the buffalo spoke, saying, "The meat that was in the rice bin and over the rice house was that of another animal. How can it be that you give more weight to the words of this stupid bird than to my words?"

"The lorikeet is indeed intelligent," the judge said.

"He speaks more often with nonsense than with sense," the farmer replied. "Ask him another question. Ask him what kind of a night we had last night."

So the judge asked the lorikeet, which replied, "Last night was dark and stormy. The wind blew, the rain poured down, and the thunder roared."

"If you remember," the farmer said, "last night was calm and clear, and the moon shone with all its brightness. Can you now condemn me for a crime on the testimony of this bird?"

The people were convinced, and the judge was convinced. They said: "No, you are innocent, and your life was endangered by the witless testimony of the lorikeet. Henceforth we will not keep this bird in our houses and care for him as though he were one of us."

So the man who stole the buffalo was freed, and the lorikeet was expelled and sent back into the forest. The lorikeet lived as he had before he had known man, fending for himself and caring for his own needs.

But one day the lorikeet saw a new bird in the forest, larger than himself and covered with brilliant red and green feathers. He spoke to the new bird, asking him who he was.

"I am the parrot," the bird answered. "I have come from the South, and now I am going to live in this country. I speak the language of man."

Then the lorikeet said, "Welcome to the country. As you are a stranger here, accept my advice and warning. I too speak the language of man. For many years I was kept in man's house and cared for. I saw with my eyes and heard with my ears. I spoke not only words that man spoke, but what was in my own mind as well. But when I said what was in my own mind it displeased man, and I was driven away. This is my warning: When man learns that you can speak his language, he will capture you and bring you into his house. Say nothing but what he teaches you. Repeat his words and nothing more. For man loves to hear only his own thoughts repeated. He is not interested in truth or wisdom from any other source."

The parrot listened to the lorikeet and thanked him. And it came about as the lorikeet had predicted. Man learned of the arrival of the talking parrot, and the parrot was captured and brought to man's house. He was fed and cared for, as once the lorikeet had been cared for, and he was taught the things that man wanted him to say.

But fearful of ever saying his true thoughts lest man resent them, the parrot only echoes the words that he hears from man's lips.

THE PRIEST AND THE PEAR TREE
[China]

In the market place of the village one day there was a farmer with a cartload of beautiful pears. People crowded around his cart to see his pears, for they were very wonderful to look at, and he was known for miles around for the quality of his fruit. The farmer also had a reputation for stinginess, and the price of the pears was high.

While the crowd stood around him in this way, a ragged-looking wandering priest came among them and looked at the pears. Very humbly he begged the farmer to give him one.

But the farmer was mean and bad-tempered, and he refused. The poor priest, undiscouraged by the rough reply he received, remained standing before the cart looking at the fruit. The farmer was greatly irritated by this, and he began to berate the priest, calling him all manner of unpleasant names. Yet the priest still remained, saying, "Countryman, there are hundreds of pears in your cart. Surely you wouldn't miss one if you gave it to me?"

Someone in the crowd spoke up then, saying to the farmer: "Why don't you give the poor man a pear? If you can't spare a good one, give him a soft one. You'll never miss it."

The farmer, urged in this way, became even more obstinate and angry.

"I have grown these pears through hard work. I have no intention of bringing them to the market to dispense charity."

Other people in the market place began to speak, some taking the side of the farmer, some taking the side of the poor priest. Their voices rose. There were arguments and shouting. The hubbub became louder. At last a man came forward and handed the farmer a coin. He said, "Do you prefer this unpleasant scene to a small act of kindness? Here is money. Give the man a pear."

The farmer handed the priest a pear. The priest took it, acknowledging the gift by a low bow. Then he addressed the crowd which stood around him.

"I am deeply puzzled how a man who has had as much good fortune as this fruit farmer can be so stingy as to refuse to give away a single pear. I who asked for it gave up everything when I became a priest. I have no money, no home, and no family. Yet what I have, I gladly share with others. For example, I have a whole tree full of pears. I beg you to stay a moment and share them with me."

"If you have so many pears, why do you come to the market and beg for one?" a man asked.

"Ah," the priest said. "I must grow them first."

He quickly ate the pear in his hand, saving from it a single seed. Then he dug a hole in the ground and placed the seed in it, covering it with loose earth. "I need a little water," he said. The people in the crowd laughed, but a small boy quickly brought a pot of water and gave it to the priest, who poured it on the ground.

And suddenly they saw a tiny green sprout push its way

39

through the earth. It grew taller swiftly. Branches appeared on it, and leaves came out on the branches. The sprout became a tree, which grew taller and taller. More leaves came out, then buds, then pear blossoms. The pear blossoms fell off, leaving behind them tiny pears, which swelled until they became full grown. The beautiful fruit weighed the branches down, so many were there.

The crowd applauded with delight. The priest, his face shining with pleasure, picked the pears one by one and handed them out to the people as presents. The fruit farmer who had refused to give anything to the priest stood with his mouth open. Finally the priest picked the last pear from the miraculous tree and gave it away. Then he took the hatchet which hung on his back and chopped the tree down. He took the tree on his shoulder and walked away from the market, leaving the crowd chewing on pears.

The fruit farmer with the cart of pears, like all the others, watched the poor priest until he was out of sight. Then the farmer turned back to his cart. He saw with horror that the cart was empty. Every single pear had disappeared!

In a flash he understood what had happened. The pears the old priest had given away so generously had come out of the cart. They were the pears of the fruit farmer. As he stood there trying to figure out the full extent of the calamity, the fruit farmer saw that one of the handles of the cart was missing. He looked more closely and observed that it had been hacked off, as though by a hatchet. So this was what the priest had been chopping before he left!

The fruit farmer was in a great rage. He ran out of the market place after the priest. He did not find him, but lying in the street against a wall he saw the broken cart handle.

When the people in the market place fully understood the joke of the wandering priest, there was a great uproar. Only the stingy fruit farmer failed to join in the laughter. As for the old priest, he was never seen in that part of the country again.

THE FOUR YOUNG MEN

[Burma]

In a certain village there lived four young men, and they could make up strange and impossible tales. One day they saw a traveler resting in the rest house outside the village, and he was wearing fine clothes. The four young men plotted to take these fine clothes away from him, so they went to the rest house and started a conversation.

After a while one of the young men suggested that they all join in a contest.

"Let each one of us tell about his most wonderful adventure," he said. "Anyone who doubts the truth of the story will become the slave of the man who tells it."

The traveler agreed to the idea, and the young men smiled to themselves, thinking him to be a fool. He did not look as though he could tell impossible stories, but even so they couldn't lose the contest if they merely said they believed his tale. On the other hand, they expected their own tales would be so thoroughly unbelievable that the traveler would have to protest. They did not really intend to make the traveler their slave, but merely to claim his clothes, since the property of a slave was the property of his master. So they went to the village and brought back the headman to act as a judge of the contest.

The first young man then began his wonderful adventure:

"Before I was born, my mother asked my father to pick

some plums from the tree in front of the house, but my father replied that the tree was too high to climb. My mother asked my brothers, but they gave the same answer. I couldn't bear to see my mother disappointed, so I climbed the tree and picked the plums myself when no one was looking. I left them on the kitchen table. No one knew where the plums had come from, but my mother was very pleased."

The young man looked at the traveler, hoping that he would express doubt as to the truth of the story, but he merely nodded his head to show that he believed it. The other three young men also nodded their heads.

So it was the second young man's turn, and he said:

"When I was a week old, I took a walk in the forest and saw a large date tree with ripe fruit on it. As I was very hungry, I climbed up the tree swiftly and began eating dates. When I had eaten all I could hold, I was so heavy and sleepy that I couldn't climb down. So I went back to the village and brought a ladder. I propped it against the tree and came down by its rungs. If I hadn't found the ladder, I would still be up in the date tree."

He looked at the traveler, expecting to hear some protest, but the traveler merely nodded his head in agreement. So did the other three young men.

It was the third young man's turn to tell his impossible adventure:

"When I had reached the ripe old age of one year, I saw a rabbit running swiftly into the tall grass, and I chased it. When I caught up with it, I discovered that what I had been chasing was really a tiger. He opened his mouth to swallow me. I told him this was very unfair, because what

I was looking for was a rabbit and not a tiger. But he took no notice of my protests and opened his mouth even wider. Becoming annoyed at his rudeness, I caught hold of him with my left hand and broke him in two."

Again the young men looked expectantly at the traveler, waiting for him to deny the truth of the story. But he nodded his head in agreement. So the fourth young man told his story:

"Last year I went fishing in a boat, but I couldn't catch a single fish. I asked the other fishermen and they hadn't caught any fish either. I decided to see what was the matter at the bottom of the river. I dived out of my boat and swam down. After about three days I reached the bottom of the river, and I discovered a fish as large as a mountain there, eating all the small fish. I killed the great fish with one blow of my fist. After all this exercise I was beginning to feel a little hungry, so I decided to eat the fish right there. I lit a fire and after roasting the fish I ate it at one sitting. Then I floated back up to my boat and went home."

The young men waited for the traveler to laugh at this monstrous tale, or to cry out, "Oh, this is unbelievable!" but he merely nodded his head in agreement.

And then it was his turn to tell of an adventure. He began:

"Some years ago I had a farm. There was one fruit tree on my farm which grew differently from the others. It had four branches but no leaves. On the end of each branch, however, was a single fruit. When they were ripe, I picked the four fruits, and when I cut them open a young man jumped out of each one of them. As they came from my tree, they were legally my property—that is to say, my slaves. I made them work on my farm. But being lazy and much preferring to sit around and tell tales than to work, they ran away after only a few weeks. Since that time I have been traveling all over the country looking for them. And I am very gratified that now, here in this rest house, I have found them at last. Young men, you know very well that you are my runaway slaves. Come back with me to my farm, and don't give me any trouble."

The four young men couldn't say a word. They couldn't shake their heads one way or another. They were greatly embarrassed, for they were in a hopeless position. If they declared that the man's story was true, they would be acknowledging that they were his runaway slaves. If they said the story was false, they would lose the contest and become his slaves anyway. So they were silent.

The headman of the village asked them whether they believed the traveler's tale or not. They were silent. He asked them again. They would not speak. Once more he asked. They remained mute.

And so the headman declared that the stranger had won the contest. The traveler said to the young men, "Now you are my slaves. Since you are my slaves, your clothes belong to me. Take off your clothes and give them to me. After that I will give you your freedom."

The young men removed their clothes and gave them to him. The traveler tied the clothes in a bundle, put it on his back, and resumed his journey, while the four clever young men stood naked in the rest house.

THE VALIANT POTTER

[*India*]

A tiger was once wandering near a village when a violent storm arose, bringing with it thunder, lightning, wind, and rain. For shelter, the tiger crept close to the wall of a small hut on the edge of the village. Inside the hut, the old woman who lived there was also concerned with the storm, for the roof was full of holes and the rain leaked through in many places. As the water dripped inside, the old woman ran from place to place, moving the furniture here and there to save it from the rain. Lying with his ear to the wall, the tiger heard this great commotion inside. He heard things being dragged about, and he heard the old woman wailing and talking to herself. He heard her say: "Oh, it is awful! This perpetual dripping! Is there no escape from it? For a while life is peaceful and quiet, and then the perpetual dripping is upon me! It is terrible, terrible!"

Then came the sound of more rattling and scraping as the furniture was pulled around again, while the old woman wailed, "Stop, stop, it is killing me!" The tiger was deeply impressed by what he heard.

"I wonder what Perpetual Dripping is?" he thought. "It must be a dreadful thing!" And hearing the screech of heavy furniture being pulled across the floor he said,

"What a terrible noise!   *That* must be the fearful creature that is called Perpetual Dripping!"

And so the tiger huddled against the wall, quite worried by what was going on, waiting for the rain to stop so that he could go away.

Just at this moment a potmaker came along the dark road looking for his donkey, which had run away in the storm. The lightning flashed, and he saw a large animal lying by the old woman's hut.   Mistaking it for his donkey, he rushed up to the tiger, grabbed it by one ear, and began to kick it and beat it in anger.

"You miserable animal!" he shouted.   "I have to go out looking for you in the pouring rain on a night like this!" He abused the tiger some more with his stick.   "Get up on your feet immediately, or I'll break your bones!"   His rage increased.   He kicked and shouted.   The tiger was bewildered.   No one had ever done this to him before. He became frightened.   Then it dawned on him that this must be the Perpetual Dripping the old woman was talking about.   "No wonder the woman was worried!" the tiger said to himself.

The tiger got to his feet.   The potter, still thinking he was dealing with his donkey, struck the tiger a few more blows and got on his back.   Then he forced the tiger to carry him home, kicking and cursing him all the way. When he got to his house he tied the tiger by the neck and by the feet to a strong post in front of his door.   Then he went into his house and slept.

When morning came, the potter's wife went out and saw the tiger tied there.   Surprised, she went to her husband and

47

said, "Do you know what animal you brought home last night in the storm?"

"Yes," he answered, becoming angry again at the thought of it, "that miserable donkey!"

"Come and look at him," the woman said.

He arose and looked. When he saw what animal it was, his legs nearly failed to hold him up, and he felt himself all over to see if he was wounded or broken anywhere. But he found not even a scratch.

News of the potter's exploit quickly spread through the village, and everyone came to see the captured tiger and to hear how it had been caught and subdued. The story was soon told in other villages and finally it came to the Raja of the country. So astonished was the Raja with the tale of a man riding a tiger that he went to the potter's house himself.

When he arrived with his attendants, he found the story to be true. Even more amazing was the fact that this tiger was a fierce one which had been terrorizing the countryside. The Raja was so impressed that he then and there conferred on the potter a title. He gave him an estate, with many houses and much land, and he made him a general in the army and gave him ten thousand cavalry troops to command.

The potter and his wife began to lead a new life of luxury and ease. But shortly afterward, word came that a foreign king was riding with a great army to conquer the country. The Raja acted swiftly. He called his important military chiefs together so that he might appoint one of them commander-in-chief. But none of them wanted to accept such grave responsibility. They said the country was so badly prepared for the emergency that it was doubtful that they could drive the enemy away. Then the Raja thought of the valiant potter who had ridden on the back of the tiger. He sent for him, and when the potter arrived the Raja said: "I appoint you commander-in-chief of my armies. It is up to you to turn back the enemy."

The potter was appalled at what had happened to him. But he said, "I accept the responsibility. But first I must go alone to examine the enemy forces."

The Raja agreed, and the potter went home to his wife. He told her what had occurred, saying, "This is a difficult thing for me. I am supposed to lead the army, but, as you know, I can't even ride a horse. You must try to find me a quiet pony, so that I won't fall off. Meanwhile, I have managed to delay things until tomorrow."

But the following morning the Raja's messengers arrived with a large, fierce horse, saying the Raja requested the potter to ride it when he went to examine the enemy camp.

The potter was now quite frightened. The horse was strong and spirited. But he dared not refuse, so he sent the messengers back to tell the Raja he would do as the Raja wished. When they were gone, the potter asked his wife, "How will I do it? I have never been on a horse in my life."

"Don't worry," his wife said. "All you have to do is to get on. I will tie you firmly so that you can't fall off."

So the potter tried, but he didn't know how to begin. The saddle seemed too high.

"I can't get into it," the potter said.

"You'll have to jump," his wife replied.

The potter tried jumping, but he couldn't jump high enough.   Each time he jumped he fell on the ground.

"When I jump, I forget which way to turn," he said.

"You must do it so that your face is toward the horse's head," his wife explained.

"I know, I know," the potter said.   This time he jumped and came down in the saddle, but instead of facing the horse's head he was facing the horse's tail.

"No, no," his wife said, helping him down again.

He began all over, slipping, falling, and getting tangled in the stirrups.   But finally, when he had given up all hope, he suddenly found himself sitting in the saddle, facing in the right direction.

"Quickly!" he shouted.   "Tie me before I fall off!"

His wife brought some rope and tied his feet in the stirrups.   She tied the stirrups together under the horse.   She tied a rope around his waist and fastened it to the saddle. She put a rope around his shoulders and tied it to the horse's tail and to the horse's neck.

By now the horse was nervous with all that was going on. He began to run.   The potter called out.

"Wife!   Wife!   You forgot to tie my hands!"

"Hold on to the horse's mane!" she shouted.

The potter caught hold of the horse's mane and hung on desperately, while the animal thundered across the fields. They went this way and that way, over ditches and walls, across rice fields and fences.   The potter had nothing to do with where the horse went, he just clung in fright, though he couldn't have dismounted if he'd wanted to.

When he saw where the galloping horse was taking him he was even less happy than before, for they were going directly toward the camp of the enemy.

"This must not happen!" the potter cried out. And as they passed a small banyan tree growing in the plain, he reached out his hand and seized it, thinking to pull himself loose from the horse. But the horse was going too fast, and the earth in which the tree was growing was soft, so that the tree came out by its roots. Thus the desperate potter rode on in a wild gallop into the enemy camp with the banyan tree in his hand.

The soldiers of the camp had seen him coming. They had seen him ride directly and fearlessly at them. They had seen him pull up a tree by the roots, and they saw him brandishing it like a club. And thinking him to be merely the advance guard of an entire army, they scattered in panic, shouting to one another. "Run for your lives! These are not men, but gigantic monsters!"

Seeing his men in flight, the enemy King quickly wrote a letter to the Raja of the country, saying that he was calling off the invasion and proposing a treaty of peace. Then he also mounted his horse and fled.

As they disappeared, the potter's horse charged into the middle of the camp, and just at this moment the ropes that held him broke and the exhausted potter fell on the ground. The horse, too tired to run any more, stopped and at last stood still.

When the potter got up he found that the camp was deserted, and in the King's tent he found the letter written to his Raja. So he took the letter and returned home, leading the horse by the bridle, for he had no intention of ever riding again.

When he reached home, his wife came out to meet him. He said, "Ah, wife, since I left here I have ridden far and had great and terrible adventures! Take this letter to the Raja, and take the horse with you, for I want nothing more to do with him."

So the wife took the letter and returned the horse to the Raja. The Raja read the letter saying the enemy forces had gone away. And the wife explained to him that her husband was just then too weary from his battle to come, but that he would arrive in the morning.

The next day the potter came on foot, grateful that he didn't have a horse under him. When the people saw him coming, they said, "There is a brave man! He turned back an entire army single-handed. And he is as modest as he is brave. After putting the enemy to flight, he walks simply and humbly, instead of riding pompously as any other man would do!"

The potter was received by the Raja with honors. And he is still remembered as the man who fearlessly rode a tiger and valiantly destroyed an army of invaders.

FOUR RIDDLES
[*Pakistan*]

There was once a poor woodcutter who owned little in life except a reputation for wisdom and understanding of mysteries. People spoke often about this man with great respect, repeating to each other wise things he had said or done. Even the King heard of him, at first only now and then, and later more often, to the point where he was annoyed.

"Can this poor woodcutter be as wise and shrewd as people say?" he asked his ministers one day.

"Who can tell?" they answered. "Why don't you put him to a test?"

"Tell me about him," the King said.

"There is little to tell," one of the ministers replied. "He is simply a humble man with four sons. But it is said that he can answer any riddle that is known."

The King's curiosity was aroused. "Any riddle that is known!" he repeated. "But what about riddles that are unknown?"

He then sent for the most powerful fakir in the land, a dervish who was able to perform feats of magic. And he instructed him this way:

"This woodcutter with the four sons, I want you to devise the most curious and difficult riddles to test him. If he is less wise than people say, he must be silenced, for in that case he is the cause of false rumors. But if he is able to survive the tests you give him, I will see to it that he is less poor than before."

The fakir made the journey to the part of the country where the woodcutter lived. He went to the place where the man usually felled his trees, and there he sat on his rug and waited.

On that day the woodcutter wasn't well, and he sent his oldest son to do his work. The young man came into the woods, and he saw there the fakir, sitting in an attitude of devout contemplation.

"Venerable person," the young man said, "I see that you are wise. Can you divine what my future will be?"

The fakir replied: "I can divine it. But first you must explain to me a thing which I will show you."

"I will try," the young man said.

So the fakir called upon the magic powers at his command and caused a strange scene to appear. The woodcutter's son suddenly saw before him a garden of grain, and around the garden was a fence made of sticks. He looked in wonder at this sight. As he watched, however, the sticks which made up the fence changed into reaping knives. They leaped among the grain stalks and cut them all down, until the garden was simply a blighted wasteland. Then the scene faded away, and the young man saw only the trees around him again.

"Well," the fakir said, "explain this thing to me."

"I can't explain it," the woodcutter's son said. "It was a strange sight without meaning."

"Now I can reveal what your future will be," the fakir said. "You are destined to be a stone."

And he turned the young man into a stone.

When the oldest son failed to return, the woodcutter became anxious. On the following morning, he sent his second son out to find his lost brother. The second son came to the woods and he also saw the fakir sitting there. And he asked him, "Venerable stranger, you seem devout and wise. Can you tell me where my brother is?"

The fakir replied, "I can tell you. First, however, you must be able to explain something that you will see."

He called on his magic powers, and suddenly standing before them in the woods were a cow buffalo and its young calf. But instead of the calf sucking the milk of its mother, it was the other way around. The mother was drinking milk from the calf. Then in a moment the two animals disappeared.

"Can you explain this riddle?" the fakir asked.

The woodcutter's son answered, "How can it be explained? It was something strange and contrary to nature."

"Since you cannot perceive the meaning," the fakir said, "I send you to join your lost brother."

And he turned the second son into a stone.

The next day the woodcutter sent his third son to find the other two. This young man also found the fakir sitting in the woods.

"Oh venerable one," he said, "can you tell me where I may find my lost brothers?"

"First," the fakir replied, "tell me the meaning of this thing."

And there appeared before them an old man with a huge load of firewood on his back. But though the man was carrying all he could hold, still he stopped to pick up a stick here and a stick there, wherever he saw one. Then the picture disappeared.

"What is the meaning of this riddle?" the fakir asked.

"How can anyone know?" the third son replied. "It is a meaningless thing."

"In that case you may join your brothers," the fakir said. And the third son also was turned into a stone.

The following morning, the anxious woodcutter sent his youngest son to find the other three. In the woods the young man encountered the fakir, who presented him with a fourth riddle. There appeared a large pond, and water was flowing from it into smaller ponds. As the youngest son watched, the large pond emptied itself and became dry. Then the scene vanished and the fakir asked, "What is the meaning?"

"I don't understand the meaning," the young man said.

"Then," the fakir declared, "you may join your brothers." And like them the youngest son turned into a stone.

When the youngest son failed to return, the woodcutter arose from his bed and went out into the woods to see what had happened. He came to where the fakir was waiting for him, and he asked, "Learned and devout man, have you seen my four sons?"

"Yes," the fakir said. "In the name of the King I have silenced them, because false rumors of shrewdness in your family have caused too much talk."

He pointed to the four stones standing in a row.

"Why do you mistreat the innocent?" the woodcutter asked. "Have they boasted or made trouble?"

"They are of your family," the fakir said, "and they could not answer the riddles. Had they been able to do so I would have left them as they were. Yet if you yourself can answer the riddles I will bring back your sons."

"I will try," the woodcutter said.

So the fakir called up the scene of the garden with the fence of sticks. The sticks turned into reaping knives and destroyed the grain. When the scene ended, the woodcutter said:

"This picture depicts a person in whose care some money has been placed; and when the rightful owner asks for it the guardian of the money spends it so that he won't have to give it back."

As he finished speaking these words, one of the stones disappeared, and in its place was the woodcutter's oldest son.

The fakir then called up the scene of the buffalo cow and calf, and again the calf was giving milk to its mother.

"This reminds me of a lazy woman who lives off the work of her daughter," the woodcutter said.

And instantly another stone disappeared, and in its place stood his second son.

Then came the scene of the old man with a great load of wood on his back. As before, the man kept gathering and gathering, though he had more than plenty.

"Isn't this the picture of people who are never satisfied with what they have?" the woodcutter said. "They go on and on, accumulating wealth far beyond their needs."

As he said this another stone disappeared, and in its place stood the third son.

The fakir then called up the last scene, with the large pond emptying itself into smaller ponds until it was dry.

"This is the unfortunate way of the world," the woodcutter said. "Often it is that a person gives all he has to help others and gets nothing in return."

The fourth stone too disappeared, and all four sons were there with their father.

The fakir said to the woodcutter, "Now, in truth, I can foretell something of the future. Had you failed to answer the riddles, there would be five stones here for future generations of woodcutters to sharpen their axes on. As it turned out, the King is pleased to have so shrewd a man as one of his subjects. Your future is to be less poor than before."

And so it was, for when the King heard about the woodcutter's infallible answers to the riddles, he sent him a bag of gold.

ASIAN

AND AFRICAN

MIDDLE EAST

THE SILVER ON THE HEARTH
[*Afghanistan*]

There was once a poor farmer who found it a great struggle to get ahead a little in the world. Though he worked very hard and lived frugally, it was impossible for him to save money from year to year. After a lifetime of labor he was no better off, it seemed, than he was on the day he was born.

One morning while he kneeled on the floor performing his morning prayers he pleaded with God for help. "Oh God," he said, "I beg you to give me riches! If I am ever to own something in this hard world, it will have to come from you! Give me riches here on my own hearth!"

And after his prayer, he arose and went about his daily tasks in the fields.

It happened one day while he was working that he caught his clothes on some brambles in the field and tore them. So that this wouldn't happen again, the man dug a little around the roots and pulled the brambles out of the ground. As he did so, he uncovered a large earthen jar. In great excitement, he dug a little more and then removed the lid of the jar. He found that the jar was filled to the brim with silver coins. At first he was exultant, but after a few minutes of thought he said:

"Oh God, I begged you for riches on my hearth, but I have found this money out here in the open fields. Therefore I shall not take it, for if it were your will for me to be rich you would have given it to me on my hearth, as I asked in my prayer."

So the man left the treasure where he had found it and went home. When he arrived, he told his wife about his discovery. The woman was angry at her husband's foolishness in leaving the riches in the field. When her husband lay down to sleep, she went out to the house of a neighbor and told him all about it, saying, "My stupid husband found a hoard of money in the fields, but the blockhead refuses to bring it home. Go and get it for yourself, and share with me."

The neighbor was very pleased with the suggestion, and he went out to find the treasure where the woman had described it. There, where the bramble bush had been uprooted, was the earthen jar. He took it from the ground and opened it. But when he lifted the lid he saw not silver, but a jarful of poisonous snakes.

Into the man's mind rushed the thought, "Ah, that woman must be my enemy! She hoped I would put my hand in the jar to be bitten and poisoned!"

So he replaced the lid and carried the jar back home with him, just as he had found it. When night came he went to the house of the poor farmer, climbed on the roof, and emptied the jar of poisonous snakes down the chimney.

When dawn came, the poor farmer who had first discovered the jar got up to perform his prayers. As the morning rays of the sun fell upon the hearth, his eyes opened wide. For the hearth was covered with silver coins. His heart swelled with gratitude, and he gave thanks to God, saying, "Now, Oh God, I accept these riches, knowing that you intend for me to have them, for you have placed them upon my own hearth, as I requested!"

THE QUIVERING NEEDLE
[*Iran*]

Once the Mullah, or teacher, named Nasr-ed-Din was walking through the great covered bazaar of Isfahan. He bowed to right and left as he recognized friends buying, selling, or merely bargaining. He loved the excitement of the bazaar where he could always meet someone just back from a journey—from Tabriz or Hamadan, possibly from faraway India or Egypt.

Where two of the covered streets of the bazaar met, he found a group of men with their heads close together over something held in the hand of a camel driver named Musa. As the Mullah naturally wished to know what was going on, his turbaned head was soon in the huddle.

"Salam," the men greeted him.

"Salam," the Mullah replied.

"We were wondering what this strange thing is," one of the men told the Mullah. "When Musa was riding his camel across the desert, he saw it shining on the ground."

"I climbed down from my camel," Musa took up the story, "and I picked it up. But I do not know what it is. I thought that some of the wise men in the bazaar could tell me. But nobody can guess."

"You know everything, Mullah." It was Mustapha speaking. "Can you tell us what it is?"

Mullah Nasr-ed-Din stared at the small round box of

metal and glass in the palm of Musa's sun-browned hand. Inside the box he saw letters and a tiny needle. It was this needle that was most strange. It quivered as the box was turned, but always it came to rest pointing in the same direction. The Mullah took the little box in his hand. He turned it this way and that. The needle quivered, but always it pointed to the north. The Mullah stroked his beard in the way he did when he was thinking his hardest. Then he handed the little box back to Musa.

"What is it?" the camel driver asked. The men waited hopefully for an answer. They expected wise and knowing words from the learned Mullah. They were all most curious about the quivering needle that had a magic way of always pointing north no matter how much it was twisted and turned.

For a moment the Mullah stroked his beard and said nothing. Then he did a most amazing thing. First he cried. Then he laughed. He repeated this as long as the men could stand watching him—crying and laughing, laughing and crying, crying and laughing.

"Why are you crying?" asked some of the men.

"Why are you laughing?" asked others.

"Nobody, not even a Mullah, should cry and laugh at the same time," said Mustapha.

"I'll tell you why I am crying and why I am laughing," promised the Mullah.

By this time every man and boy in that part of the great covered bazaar was crowding close to the Mullah to hear what wise thing he would say. Those who did not know the Mullah were being told about him by those who did.

Women, drawing their veils over their faces, made up errands to keep them in that part of the bazaar.

"I am crying," began the Mullah, "because not one of you is smart enough to name this little round box with its quivering needle. How very stupid of you all! I am ashamed for you. Do you wonder that I cry?"

The Mullah looked from man to man. They withered under his scorn for their ignorance. Even the boys squirmed and drooped in their shame at knowing so little. The women sighed under their veils, glad that they were not expected to know very much beyond the care of their houses and their children. They did not wonder that the learned Mullah was ashamed that the people of the great city of Isfahan were so stupid.

Mustapha, who knew the Mullah better than the others did, was brave enough to change the subject.

"You have told us why you are crying," he said. "Now, good Mullah, will you tell us why you are laughing?"

The Mullah laughed once more.

"I am laughing," he said, "because I also do not know what it is."

THE STORK CALIPH

[Iraq]

There was once a Caliph, grand ruler of the ancient Bagdad, who enjoyed a long beard, a golden water pipe, the love of his people, and a cook who prepared the most luscious fresh fish ever known. Moreover, this remarkable Caliph could sit for hours on one leg with the other thrust straight out before him; he could repeat the whole of the Koran; and he could tell his subjects exactly the core of their heated discussions in the bazaar the day before. The people of Bagdad whispered that their Caliph had twenty eyes and thirty ears.

Every morning the Caliph received petitioners in his great palace, but during the afternoon he was not to be seen by any man, for he gave out the word that he spent the latter part of the day in siesta. But the citizens of Bagdad did not know of a tiny door which led from the palace into a quiet lane.

"Come, Ali Ben Manzar," called the Caliph to his Grand Vizier. "It is time for us to collect news of our subjects. We will go into the bazaar."

Ali Ben Manzar picked up two merchants' costumes, which speedily changed the mighty Caliph and his Vizier into dealers in silks, and they went into the city of Bagdad as was their secret custom.

But as they turned towards the city an old peddler, withered as a brown leaf, glanced at them keenly once before he dropped his eyelids and thrust under their noses, with his shaking claw, a handsome jeweled box.

The Caliph halted, attracted by its beauty.

"What are you selling, father?" he inquired.

"Snuffboxes, worthy Caliph."

"How much do you charge for them?"

"One piece of gold, glorious Caliph."

The Caliph threw him two pieces of gold and took the snuffbox. It glittered and sparkled in the late afternoon sun as the Caliph and his Vizier walked away. Presently they came to a quiet lake on the outskirts of the city, and the Caliph, who felt somewhat fatigued, thought that it would be well perhaps to rest on the shore for a time, before returning by way of the bazaars to his palace. He held out the snuffbox and laughed.

"I have bought this box for two gold pieces and should like a sniff. I shall see if it contains snuff."

He opened the lid and saw the tiny opening filled with a brownish dust. But as the Caliph reached for a pinch he perceived a small piece of parchment fitted neatly into the inside of the lid. He drew it forth curiously and found it to be folded three times. He slowly read aloud:

"A sniff of snuff gives thee wings,
A cry Csalavér gives thee hands."

"Ah," said the Vizier, thinking this a fine joke, "the box is magic, glorious Caliph. Let us try the snuff."

"But," objected the Caliph, "do you believe that the written word here can bring us back to our own shapes?"

"Why not," shrugged the Vizier, "if the snuff gives us wings, so must the word give us our hands."

The Caliph was sorely tempted. He looked into the cloudless sky, and longed to fly there high above his city of Bagdad. He took a pinch of snuff and held out the box to his Grand Vizier, who likewise raised a few grains to his nostrils. They sniffed long and loud. There was a sudden rustling, a feathery stirring, and the Caliph saw before him a large stork standing with wings outspread. He opened his mouth to laugh and to say, "So the charm worked for you, Ali Ben Manzar!"

But all that came from the mouth of the Caliph was a hoarse, "Kalap! Kalap!"

The Vizier flapped his wings and opened his beak widely, but all that he said was, "Kalap! Kalap!"

However, having become birds, the Caliph and his Grand Vizier understood the language of the air.

"Kalap! Kalap! Let us fly above the lake!" squeaked the Caliph.

"Kalap! Kalap! That is a good idea," clacked the Grand Vizier.

And so they spread their wide white wings and soared, with a rare taste of freedom, above the water, and across the city, where the Caliph saw his people praying and sleeping, talking and fighting, selling and buying. He observed with his small eyes the servants of his palace, and the soldiers of his army.

"Truly," thought the flying Caliph, "a stork of the air knows more of my city than I do."

68

As evening drew close about the large birds, the Grand Vizier swooped near enough to his master to screech into his face: "Glorious Caliph, we must return to the palace, for night draws near, and we shall be missed."

The Caliph, so much was he enjoying his flight, did not wish to return, but he felt, with a sigh, that Ali Ben Manzar was right. They wheeled with a sweep of rustling wings toward the secluded lake, where they settled to earth and stood on their long and spindling legs.

The Caliph, who had hidden his snuff box under a low bush, drew it forth and read again the magic word. He raised his beak.

"Csalavér!" he croaked, and turned his eyes toward his Grand Vizier, expecting to see before him the brown familiar face and turbaned head of Ali Ben Manzar. But the Caliph could scarcely stand in his amazement, for the Grand Vizier was not there. There was only the big, feathered form of a stork.

"Csalavér!" he screamed in horror. "Csalavér! Csalavér!"

But storks they remained.

The Grand Vizier was terrified. He flapped his wings and ruffled his feathers and stood first on one foot and then on the other. He opened his pointed beak and uttered a cry.

"Csalavér! Csalavér!"

The smooth water of the lake showed not a ripple, and the air echoed the sounds of two storks, who seemed beside themselves with terror. They flew about, filling the evening with raucous noises and broken feathers which they tore out in their frenzy. Then they grew tired and decided to settle down quietly and talk the situation over.

"Ali Ben Manzar," spoke the stork Caliph sadly, "it seems that some enemy has contrived to outwit us. What can be done to relieve our plight?"

"Noble Caliph," answered the weary Vizier, "I know of nothing. We must continue to live as birds until we can discover the right word to bring us back to our own shapes."

And so the Caliph of Bagdad and his Grand Vizier searched hungrily along the reeds, where they thrust their long beaks into the silent water and plucked forth their meal of fish. As the moon rose above the city of Bagdad, it stared in surprise at two large storks which slept, side by side, in the shallows of the lake.

At the earliest gleam of gray dawn, the Caliph and his Grand Vizier spread their wings and soared anxiously above Bagdad to observe what excitement was caused by their disappearance. They settled above the palace to watch the wild astonishment of the courtiers and servants who searched in every possible corner of the grounds and gardens as well as the buildings. The Caliph swooped low to hear what they were shouting.

"Ah," cried a slave, "the very birds of the air come to help us seek our master, who must have been seized by demons."

The Caliph flew away, somewhat consoled, for he knew that the people grieved for him.

Next morning the officials of the palace were obliged to announce in the market place that the Lord Caliph and his

Grand Vizier had disappeared, no man knew where. There rose to the storks overhead a prolonged cry of grief and terror, which filled the heavens like a roll of summer thunder.

The birds went again to their lake, and every night they slept on one leg, after a supper of fish.

Weeks passed, and the storks still flew about the city anxiously. One day, as they sailed slowly above a highway which led from the neighboring kingdom into Bagdad, the birds saw below them a long procession of riders, decked in brilliant silks, who sat upon camels and horses which trailed colored shawls in the dust of the road. Servants and slaves walked beside the riders. The Caliph grew suspicious. He swooped quickly down until his wings almost brushed the astonished head of the first horseman, who wore the robes of a prince. The Caliph rose again, uttering a harsh clack from his open beak.

"Ali Ben Manzar," he cried, "this prince is no other than the son of Kadhur, who has always wished us ill! I think little good can come of his arrival in leaderless Bagdad."

All the way to the city the storks flew around and around in the air. When the procession reached the palace and went confidently through its gates, the storks flapped their wings wildly. The Caliph watched, almost holding his breath, and saw the doors swing open. From the palace came an obsequious body of courtiers and retainers, followed by slaves, who bowed to the ground before the prince. The lord inclined his head haughtily and spoke.

"My noble father, Kadhur Khan of the neighboring kingdom, has received word that your exalted Caliph and ruler of Bagdad is dead. Knowing that the august Caliph had no

71

heirs, the Khan has sent me, his youngest son, to live in your city and be your lord."

The palace officials bowed respectfully, while from the crowd, which had followed the strangers through the streets and was now jammed about the gates, came a long shout of joy.

"Long live the new Caliph!"

"Come," spoke the Vizier, "it does not avail us to remain here now. Our city is lost, for the son of Kadhur Khan can only be an evil man. Let us fly to the deep forest where we may find peace."

Over the lake the big birds sailed and beyond the hills to a forest, which was cool and dark and quiet and which filled them with a sad peace. They lived on small fish from a brook, and they did not speak of Bagdad or of the new Caliph.

When some months had passed, the Grand Vizier, as was his usual daily habit, was searching out food. He left the Caliph standing mournfully on one leg to follow a tiny, tender, green frog which eluded him hop after hop. The Grand Vizier found himself suddenly in a distant part of the wood which neither of the storks had ever visited before. Not a ray of sunshine penetrated the dark green depths. Nothing moved, there seemed to be no faintest breeze, and absolute silence enveloped the forest like a smothering veil.

The Vizier shivered and could not restrain a jump of fright when he heard a sharp sound. It seemed to be a quick tapping immediately before him, but he could see nothing. Quietly the stork moved forward, and was instantly relieved to perceive that the noise was made by a woodpecker, whose red head moved spasmodically up and down as she drove her little beak into the bark of a tree. Ali Ben Manzar stared, and was amazed, for as the little bird prodded methodically into the trunk large round tears, glittering like silver, rolled from her eyes and dropped with tiny splashes on the leaves. The Grand Vizier quietly withdrew and returned to his master to tell him what he had seen. Flying across the tops of trees, the two storks went back to the quiet spot to observe the woodpecker together. The Caliph, who had thought that nothing could surprise him again, was astonished to see the small bird with tears rolling from its eyes. He advanced.

"Good woodpecker," he clacked, "can you understand the words of a stork?"

The little bird turned her brilliant head towards the intruders.

"Who are you?" she chirped.

"Then you understand our language? This is indeed fortunate. Why do you weep as you search for worms?" the Caliph asked.

"Ah," answered the bird in a voice choked with sobs, "I have good cause to weep, stork. You have always been a bird, and no doubt you enjoy this life, but I—I am forced to go in this disguise of my true self."

The storks fluttered their wings excitedly.

"What is the matter, woodpecker?" inquired the Caliph kindly.

"I have been turned into a woodpecker by the sorceries of an evil man, Kadhur Khan, who lives in the kingdom which borders this forest."

73

"So Kadhur is a sorcerer!" murmured the stork. "What can be done to change you to your original shape?"

"Because I refused to marry the evil son of that sorcerer, my fate is to remain a woodpecker until a man in human form asks me to marry him. And that can never be."

The woodpecker turned her little red head and the storks again saw tears spilling from her eyes.

"In addition to my harsh fate," sobbed the small bird, "I am forced to listen night after night to the devilish incantations of three wizards who meet with the Khan in this enchanted wood."

"Where do they meet?" asked the Caliph.

The woodpecker nodded her head toward the south.

"Straight through the trees where a circle of grass is open to the sky." She resumed her tapping with a deep sigh.

The Caliph nodded to his Grand Vizier, and, with a great flapping of wings, the two storks flew south. In the midst of the thick forest they saw beneath them a small circle of green. The big birds came to earth and hopped into the surrounding underbrush where they hid themselves. All day they stayed there, and when the moon flooded the grassy circle with pale light they were rewarded for their patience. Three men stealthily crept forward and sat with legs crossed in the circle, where they were joined by two others, who were swathed in dark cloaks. The Caliph nodded to his companion when he caught a glimpse of the squinting eyes of the Khan and the haughty profile of the young prince, the new Caliph of Bagdad.

"My son," muttered the Khan in a low voice, "how does the city of Bagdad receive you?"

"How should it receive me?" asked the young man, "I am the master there. The people are not so joyful as they were when I first arrived, but they obey. But I would like to know how you disposed of the Caliph?"

The old man grinned slyly.

"I can tell you now that my plans have worked so well. Disguised as a peddler, I sold to the Caliph and his Grand Vizier a magic snuffbox, the contents of which transformed them into storks. They tried it out, thinking the magic a fine joke, but also believing that the word written within the lid would change them again to men. But I prevented that. I substituted one letter in the word. I wrote 'Csalavér' instead of 'czalavér.' They must remain forever storks."

The son laughed.

The storks had heard enough. As soon as they could emerge without being seen, they flew back to the tree of the little woodpecker, where they had scarcely regained their footing before they repeated the magic word. They found themselves once more the Caliph and his Grand Vizier. The woodpecker looked on amazed. Then the Caliph, in all his dignity, bowed low to the small bird, and spoke.

"Fair woodpecker, I have come to ask your hand in marriage."

Before the eyes of the men the bird vanished, and they saw a slender princess, with joyful eyes, standing among the trees. She inclined her head.

"Noble Lord," she murmured, "you have made my life once more my own. Therefore I give it into your keeping."

The Caliph and his Vizier walked, one on each side of

the lovely princess, until they came to the city of Bagdad. When the people saw their kind master striding through the streets as if he had never been away, they were filled with awe and prostrated themselves to pray before him. But the Caliph did not stop. He came to the gates of the palace, where the Grand Vizier cried to the keeper, "Behold your master has returned! Open to him!"

The people of Bagdad, weary of the constant hauteur and cruelty of the new lord, set up a great shout of welcome. The keeper flung wide the gates, and soldiers assembled around their Caliph.

The son of Kadhur Khan was seized and bound and sent back to his wicked father.

In seven days the wedding of the woodpecker maiden and the stork Caliph was celebrated with great joy by the people. But the Caliph no longer sat on one leg; he folded both his legs beneath him, and in all the peaceful days of his life he could not look with pleasure upon fish. He ordered his cooks never to allow fish in the city of Bagdad for a hundred years and a day, and this command was feelingly enforced as long as he lived, by his Grand Vizier.

IMPOSSIBLE TALES
[*Syria*]

It came to the ears of the Caliph that there was in the city a storyteller of great talents, a man who could spin yarns endlessly without faltering. According to the rumors, this man could tell adventures from sunset to dawn, recite unheard of tales from sunrise until night, and never tell the same story twice.

The Caliph sent his court attendants to find the storyteller, and when they brought the man before him the Caliph said, "It is rumored that you are the greatest storyteller in the land. Why is it I have never heard of you?"

"I have no pretensions to greatness," the man replied. "I merely entertain my friends in the coffeehouse with my favorite tales."

"Come, come," the Caliph said. "Let us not begin with false modesty. It is said that you can tell every kind of tale, and spin it out until your listeners cry for you to end it. When you have had something to eat, I will listen to one of your inventions."

The court attendants fed the storyteller, and then they brought him again before the Caliph.

"If I wanted a story to last until dawn, you could tell it," the Caliph said. "If I wanted a story that was all true, I am sure you would be able to tell it. But these are not true tests, since many other storytellers can do as well.

What I want from you is merely a short tale, but everything you say must be false.   If I detect one word of truth in it, I will make you my slave.   Now you may begin."

When the storyteller heard what was expected of him, he hesitated, for it is difficult to talk for any length of time without saying something true.   But he had no choice, so he began:

"Oh great Caliph," he said, "I am my father's elder brother.   I was eight years old when he was born.   My grandmother put him in my arms and told me to keep him from crying.   But nothing I did seemed to satisfy him, until he told me to carry him to the bazaar.   There he seemed happy because he could argue with the other men over the fine points of the Koran.   Before we left the bazaar, he insisted on buying a fresh egg, but no sooner had he bought it than a chicken pecked its way out.   As the chicken was very large, and as we were both tired, we rode the chicken home.   But by the time we arrived, the chicken had grown as large as a camel, and I had to hand my father down to my grandfather who—inasmuch as my father was my brother—was also my father."

The Caliph grunted at the preposterous lie of the storyteller.

"That chicken," the storyteller went on, "had a tremendous appetite.   It ate so much that before long we were all on the verge of starvation, and we decided to put the chicken to work.   Since the chicken belonged to my father, he drove it out every morning and piled firewood on its back, until we had a vast supply of wood in our yard.   But the rubbing of the wood on the chicken's back made sores, and the chicken became sick. My grandfather became worried, and he consulted his great grandmother about what to do. She advised him to make a poultice out of a walnut seed and put it on the chicken's back. This he did. The next morning when we awoke the chicken was well again, but a walnut tree was growing out of her back. Within three days it had grown into an enormous tree which moved with the chicken wherever it went. Within a week a huge crop of walnuts was hanging in the branches. Twelve men were required to pick all the nuts, and it took them from Saturday to Thursday. The branches were spread so far that a nut picker going from the sunny side of the tree to the shady side would find the sun had set before he arrived."

The Caliph shook his head and snorted.

"When the picking was done," the storyteller went on, "I went around the tree to see if all the nuts had been removed. It took me an entire day. Just as I was about to go home, I saw my father's chicken sitting in the branches, getting ready to roost for the night. I picked up a clod of earth and threw it at her. That clod went up in the tree, but it didn't come down. It spread and spread and completely covered the top of the tree, and we were greatly elated to discover that we had forty acres of new farmland up in the air.

"We put our cattle up there to graze, and when the next plowing season came we got the new ground ready for planting. My grandfather and I planted sesame seed, but after a month we saw that nothing was growing. My grandfather asked his neighbors' advice, and they told him he had been foolish to plant sesame, that melons were the only things that would grow on freshly turned sod. So he sent me and my younger brother—that is, my father—up in the tree to pick up all the sesame seed we had sown.

"That took us about an hour. There were about eight bushels of sesame seed, but I noticed, when we were through, that one of the seeds was missing. We went back over the forty acres, looking for the missing seed, and were just ready to give up when we saw a small ant dragging it to his hill. I seized the seed, but the ant wouldn't let go. We had a furious tug of war, but neither of us could get it away from the other. In the heat of the struggle, the sesame seed broke in two. So much oil flowed from that single sesame seed that it made a river, and the people of our village were able to float their crops to the city in boats on the river of sesame oil."

Again the Caliph snorted.

"Then," the storyteller went on, "while my father, my grandfather, and I were planting the melon seeds, a terrible storm came up. As there was no shelter of any kind on this forty acres, we didn't know where to go. So my grandfather and I jumped into my father's hollow tooth. After taking one last look around him, my father took hold of a fat sheep and jumped in after us. The storm lasted forty-seven days, and we would have starved in that hollow tooth if it hadn't been for the sheep which my father had brought along.

"At last we peeked out and saw the sun was shining, but when we crawled out of the tooth we found that the rain had washed away the entire forty acres of ground and we were trapped up in the air. Fortunately, my father had had the foresight to bring a rope. We tied it securely and let it hang down to the earth; then we slid down one at a time. Thus it happened that we were saved."

And seeing that the storyteller had come to the end, the Caliph said, "This is a remarkable adventure you have related, storyteller. I have only one question to ask you: Is this tale true or false?"

"Great Caliph," the storyteller said, "it is true from beginning to end."

"If it is true," the Caliph replied, "then you have failed to do what I have asked, for I ordered you to tell a tale without a word of truth in it."

"Great Caliph," the man said, smiling, "I have followed your instructions to the letter, for when I said the tale was true I was simply telling another falsehood to round out the story."

"So be it," the Caliph said, laughing. "The rumors I have heard about your talent are well founded."

And he gave the storyteller a handful of gold pieces and sent him on his way.

THE HODJA PREACHES A SERMON
[*Turkey*]

Nasr-ed-Din Hodja one day addressed his congregation from the pulpit in the following words:

"I beseech you to tell me truly, oh Brethren, oh True Believers, if what I am going to say to you is already known to you."

And the answer came as in one voice from his congregation, that they did not know, and that it was not possible for them to know, what the Hodja was going to say to them.

"Then," the Hodja said to them, "of what possible use can it be for me to talk on an unknown subject?" And he descended from the pulpit and left the mosque, while his congregation remained in confusion.

On the following week the Hodja's congregation gathered early, because the people were greatly interested in what he might say. And rather than fewer people, there were more, for the Hodja had made a great impression in his previous appearance. The congregation was tense as the Hodja appeared.

He ascended the pulpit and said, "Oh Brethren, oh True Believers! I beseech you to tell me truly if what I am going to say to you is already known to you."

The answer that came back from the congregation was

so spontaneous as to suggest that it had been prearranged. With one voice, all together, they shouted, "Yes, Hodja, we do know what you are going to say to us!"

"If that is the case," the Hodja said, "there is no need either of you wasting your time or of me wasting my time."

And descending from the pulpit, the Hodja left the mosque. His congregation, having remained a while to pray, also left gradually, one by one and in groups. Outside the mosque they discussed the problem created by the Hodja's questions. Many of them had come not only to pray, but to hear the Hodja speak; and it appeared that he would neither deliver a sermon if they knew the subject of his talk nor if they didn't know.

On the following Friday, Nasr-ed-Din Hodja again mounted the pulpit and saw that his mosque was so crowded that not a nook or corner in it was empty. He addressed his congregation in exactly the same manner as he had before.

"Oh Brethren, oh True Believers!" he said. "I ask you to tell me truly if what I am going to say is already known to you."

And again the answer of the congregation had evidently been prepared beforehand, for one half of them rose and said, "Yes, Hodja, we do know what you are going to say to us."

And the other half of the congregation rose and said, "Oh Hodja, effendi, how could we poor ignorant people know what you intend to say to us?"

The Hodja answered: "It is well said. And now if the half that knows would explain to the other half what it is, I would be deeply grateful, for, of course, it will be unnecessary for me to say anything."

Whereupon he descended from the pulpit and left the mosque.

ABUNUWAS, THE WIT

[Saudi Arabia]

Of all men who lived in other times and are still remembered, who was the greatest trickster? There are some people who say it was this one, and some who say it was that, but those who really know say it was Abunuwas. His life was simply a long series of practical jokes and tests of wit. And when it was in his mind to do something to make people laugh, or to make a clever person look less clever, he spared neither the simple countryman nor the King himself.

It is said that one day Abunuwas's donkey was thirsty, and he needed a watering pan for the donkey to drink from. He went to his neighbor, saying, "Lend me a pot so that I can give my donkey water to drink."

His neighbor found a copper pot which he lent to Abunuwas. Abunuwas took it home and kept it three days. On the fourth day he put a little pan inside the copper pot and carried them both to his neighbor.

"Here is the pot I borrowed from you," Abunuwas said.

The neighbor took it, but when he saw the little pan nestling inside he said, "Oh, but this little pan isn't mine."

Abunuwas replied to him: "I am not a thief. What is yours I return. While I had your copper pot, it gave birth to this little pan. As the little one is the child of the big one, they both belong to you."

The neighbor saw no reason why he shouldn't profit from Abunuwas's foolishness, so he said: "Ah, that is true. Since the small one is the child of the large one, it belongs to me. The house of Abunuwas is blessed, for even the pots have children there!"

Three days later, Abunuwas again went to his neighbor and asked to borrow the pot. The neighbor thought he might again have good luck, so he gave Abunuwas his copper pot eagerly. If his pot were to have another child, what more could a man ask?

Abunuwas thanked him and took the copper pot home. But this time he didn't return the pot at all. So, after many days, the neighbor came to Abunuwas and asked for it. But Abunuwas looked very sad, and said, "I have bad news for you. Your pot is dead."

"What!" the neighbor cried out.

"Yes, I knew it would grieve you, and that is why I didn't send word when it happened."

The neighbor became indignant.

"Abunuwas, are you trying to make a fool of me? Since when does a copper pot die?"

"Didn't it give birth to a young one?" Abunuwas asked.

"Yes," the neighbor answered, thinking how he had taken the small pan.

"Everything that can produce young must someday die," Abunuwas said. "It is a sad thing that your pot died away from its own home."

Abunuwas kept the copper pot, for everywhere the neighbor told his story they said to him, "Abunuwas is right. Anything that can bring forth children is destined to die."

Another time, people say, a man came to Abunuwas and asked to borrow his donkey.

"I'm sorry," Abunuwas replied, "but my donkey isn't home today. He's gone on a little journey."

Just at that moment the donkey, which was standing behind the house, brayed loudly. The man reproached Abunuwas, saying, "Isn't that the bray of a donkey? You said your donkey was out."

"Now look here," Abunuwas said, "did you come to borrow a donkey or a bray? The donkey isn't here. But if it is a bray you want, I'll let you have one." So Abunuwas brayed: "Eee-yore! Eee-yore! Eee-yore!" And he told the startled man, "There is your bray. Climb on it quickly, and be on your way."

Once, it is said, Abunuwas built a two-story house. When it was finished, he tried to sell the house, but no one needed a place two stories high. At last Abunuwas persuaded a rich merchant to buy the top floor. The merchant moved in, and for several months Abunuwas tried to get him to buy the bottom story as well. But the merchant refused.

So one morning Abunuwas collected a large gang of laborers and brought them to the house. He ordered them to start demolishing the walls. When the merchant upstairs heard the racket, he went to the window and looked down. He saw swarms of men hacking at the walls with picks, under the direction of Abunuwas.

"What are you doing?" he shouted.

"Since I can't sell the ground floor of the house, I am knocking it down," Abunuwas said. "Better take care of your part of the building, so that it doesn't fall on my men and injure them!"

"Stop, stop!" the merchant cried out. "I'll buy. I'll buy!" And so he did. He bought the first story of the house to save the second story. Only then did Abunuwas send the workmen away.

Nor did the King fare any better at Abunuwas's hands. One night the King dreamed that there were jars of silver buried under Abunuwas's house, and the next day he promptly sent a crew of workmen to dig the treasure up. As Abunuwas wasn't home, his wife could do nothing but stand aside as the workmen dug in the floor and under the walls. When at last they concluded there was no silver buried there, the King's workmen left. Abunuwas returned and found tunnels under his walls and his floor full of holes. His wife was in tears, but Abunuwas said, "Never mind, I will pay the King back for this."

He told his wife to cook a pot of rice. When the rice was cooked, Abunuwas put some of it in a dish and covered it loosely with a napkin. He watched the flies come and settle on the napkin. He saw some of them crawl underneath to get at the rice.

The next morning, without disturbing the napkin, he took the dish and went to the King.

"I have a complaint," he told the King. "I accuse people of coming into my house uninvited and eating my food."

The King wasn't sure whether or not Abunuwas was talking in parables. He wondered whether Abunuwas was speaking of the workmen who had dug up the floor. He said sternly, "Who is it you are accusing?"

Abunuwas pulled the napkin off the dish of rice, and three flies flew out.

"These are the ones I accuse," Abunuwas said.

The King smiled.

"You are accusing flies? What do you want from me?"

"I want justice under the law," Abunuwas said. "I want permission to punish the flies."

"Very well," the King said, highly amused. "I give you the right to punish the flies. Wherever you see a fly has settled, you may strike it." And he wrote his judgement on a piece of paper and signed it with his name.

Abunuwas made a stick with a heavy knob on the end. Wherever he went he struck flies with it. If he saw flies on the dates in the market place, he would strike them and scatter the dates everywhere. If he saw flies on the fruit in the shops, he would strike them, smashing the fruit and making it worthless. When the shopkeepers protested, Abunuwas would say, "I do not hit the fruit, I hit the flies," and he would show them the order signed by the King. He went on this way for a long time, and while some people were upset by the foolishness, others thought it was quite funny. Even the King had to laugh when he heard stories of what was going on.

At last one day the King was holding court in front of his house. Abunuwas went and sat down nearby. The King was giving judgement in a lawsuit, and he was talking earnestly. While he was talking, a fly settled on his back. Abunuwas raised his stick with the heavy knob and struck the King a resounding whack. Instantly the court was in wild disorder. The people seized Abunuwas and were ready to punish him.

But he said, "If you punish me, there will be no reason or justice in it. I didn't strike the King; I struck the fly which settled on his back. And the King himself has given me permission to do this."

He showed them the order which the King had signed, and they saw it was true, and let him go.

"The flies deserve their punishment," Abunuwas said, "because they came into my house to take what wasn't theirs."

Another time, the people say, a rich merchant in the town killed a goat and prepared a feast. While the food was cooking, a poor beggar came along and saw what was happening. He sat down some distance away, down-wind from the cooking food, so that its smells were wafted to his nose. All the while that the food was cooking, the beggar sat there smelling. But the rich man didn't offer him a thing to eat.

The next day the beggar met the merchant and spoke to him, saying, "Master, you were very good to me yesterday. You let me sit nearby, and I was nourished by the smell of your goat meat, and I left feeling very well fed."

The merchant exclaimed, "That's it! That's why the goat was so tasteless! You sat there smelling up all the flavor!"

And he went before the King and accused the beggar of stealing the flavor from his goat. The King was partial to merchants, and he listened sympathetically to the complaint. He ordered the beggar to pay the merchant twelve pieces of silver.

The beggar went away and wept, for he had no money at all. He met Abunuwas and told him of the injustice. Abunuwas said, "I will help you. We will meet tomorrow morning to make a settlement of the debt."

The next day Abunuwas went to the King with the beggar. The merchant was there to receive his money.

Abunuwas asked the merchant, "You are ready to receive payment?"

The merchant answered, "Yes, I am ready."

Abunuwas took twelve pieces of silver and gave them to the beggar, saying, "Throw them on the ground."

The beggar threw the money on the ground. It tinkled as it fell on the stones.

"Did you hear the tinkle?" Abunuwas asked the merchant.

"Yes," the astounded merchant said, "I heard it."

"That is the part of the money that belongs to you," Abunuwas said. "If a man spoils food by smelling its odors, then a man can be paid by hearing the tinkle of money."

In the face of this logic, the King ruled that the merchant had received payment, and the case was closed.

THE TAIL OF ST. GEORGE'S DRAGON

[*Lebanon*]

Father Hanna was a simple, God-fearing curate in a little Christian village of Lebanon. He had been a shoemaker, and because he was the only one of the elder residents of the village who could read and write he was taken away from his shoemaker's bench and ordained to priesthood. The limit of his clerical learning, however, was reached with the recitation of the liturgy, the *pater noster*, and the *credo*. But he was prone to exaggeration, which made up for his deficiency in theology, and he often left a vivid impression on his pious congregation.

Now the chief of the village had a brilliant son, Elias, who was sent by his parents to a boarding school in Beirut. When Elias came back for his summer vacations, Father Hanna noticed that he never attended church, although when he was younger, before he had gone to the boarding school, he had been a constant attendant.

The priest was grieved at heart at the boy's retrogression, not only for the sake of his soul's salvation but because of his example before other boys of the village.

So one day Father Hanna accosted Elias on the street, and, cornering him so he couldn't escape, remonstrated with him warmly.

"My son," said the priest, "why don't you come to church

any more? I fear learning has turned you into an unbeliever."

The youth made one excuse after another, only to be met by a silencing argument from the priest. At last he blurted out, "To tell you the truth, Father, I don't go to church any more because I cannot stand your exaggerations!"

"Is *that* all, my son?" replied Father Hanna meekly. "Bless your heart, you know that I never went to any school but that of the village, and my father took me to help him in the shop when I was hardly eleven years of age. If I exaggerate, it is in good faith, for I know no better. Since you now have so much learning, why don't you come to church and give me a hint when I exaggerate, so that I may correct myself?"

The young man gladly accepted the suggestion of the priest and on the following Sunday went to church and took a seat in the very first row, just in front of the sacristy. And it happened that it was St. George's day, and Father Hanna took for his sermon the story of St. George and the dragon.

And he began, "Blessed children, what shall I tell you about St. George's dragon? Its tail alone was as long as from here to Egypt." Then, peering at Elias, he heard him give the signal they had agreed upon, "Ahem!"

So the priest, knowing he had exaggerated too much for Elias's taste, chose another spot a little closer than Egypt. "If it was not as long as from here to Egypt, at least it was as long as from here to Gaza."

Again Elias muttered: "Ahem!"

"Well, if it was not from here to Gaza, then it was from here to Jerusalem."

"Ahem!" Elias said.

"And if we do not say from here to Jerusalem, then from here to Beirut," Father Hanna said.

"Ahem!"

"If not from here to Beirut," Father Hanna said, "then from here to Juneh."

"Ahem!"

But Father Hanna had reached the limits of his patience, and under no circumstances was he willing to reduce the dragon's tail any more.

"From here to Juneh," he said firmly.

"Ahem!" Elias said.

Father Hanna leaned forward, peering at Elias, and in a gesture of resignation with out-turned palms, he said, "My son, do you want St. George's dragon to be without a tail? So be it, then, without a tail!"

THE HORSE WITHOUT A MASTER
[*Yemen*]

One day the Bedouin boy, Tamad, and his father were taking a rest in their goat-hair tent. It's black roof kept off the worst heat of the noonday sun, and they lay stretched out at ease on rugs laid over the desert sand.

There was a noise at the open front of the tent. Sa'da, the boy's horse, thrust his head in under the cloth roof. Little by little, the horse edged his way into the tent, out of the burning sun.

Tamad and his father laughed. This often happened, and usually they did not drive their favorite horses out of the cool shade.

"Sa'da knows he is well off wherever his master is," Tamad's father told him. "I know a tale about a horse that once thought he would be far better off without any master at all."

"What happened to that horse, my father?" Tamad asked.

"Praise Allah who made all things," his father began. "It took place in the days when horses could talk. Now, this horse was not happy and gentle like Sa'da. His spirit was wild. He wanted above all things to be free. He complained to the other horses. He complained to the camels. But the only answer he got from the animals was,

95

'You are a fool, oh horse.   You do not know when you are well off.'

"Then the horse complained to his master, saying, 'What is the reason that I should have to carry you here and carry you there?   Am I not bigger?   Am I not stronger than you?   A man is a poor weak creature compared to a horse. Why should I do your bidding?'

" 'I am indeed smaller, oh horse,' his owner replied, 'and I am not nearly as strong as you.   But yet you cannot do without me in the desert.   Perhaps it is different in other lands, but the desert can be cruel.   I give you your food. I find you green grass to graze on.   I bring you barley and warm camel's milk.   I even share my tent with you.   I search out water holes for you, so that you will not be thirsty. In return for the care I give you, isn't it just that you should carry me on my journeys?'

" 'It is true that you care for me,' the horse replied, 'but you also make me your slave.   I am never permitted to come and go as I like.   You put a hard bit in my mouth.   You tie on my saddle with tight ropes that bite into my belly. You make me gallop and gallop until my legs crumple with weariness.   You even ride me into battle so that sometimes I am wounded.   Who gave you the right thus to take my freedom away?'

" 'I cannot say who has given man the right,' the owner answered.   'As long as history it has been so.   Perhaps it is Allah, the Lord of Heaven and Earth, who made man the master.   But if you are so earnest in your desire to be free, I will not hold you.'

"He took off the horse's bridle.   He took off the saddle.

And he took off the camel-hair rope with which the horse was tethered. With a whinny of joy, the horse galloped away. His master was camped in a grassy part of the desert. It was then early spring. There were green bushes growing on all sides. So the horse had little trouble in getting enough food to keep him alive. There was a stream of water in the river bed nearby. He could drink whenever he liked. Oh, it was fine to be free.

"But time passed, and summer came. Under the heat of the desert sun, the green grass turned brown. The stream in the river bed became a thin trickle. At last the grass was burned up, and all the water was gone. Gone too was the camp of the horse's master. The other horses and the camels had long since been led away to better pastures and watering places.

"The horse grew hungry and thirsty. He went this way and that way. But no water or green grass could he find. The wild animals that roamed in the desert were hungry too. Foxes, hyenas, and lean hungry wolves prowled in search of something to eat and drink.

"One night in the moonlight the horse saw dark shapes creeping toward him. His keen smell told him the dark shapes were wolves looking for meat. With a whinny of fear he galloped away. But hungry wolves, too, can run very fast. They ran more swiftly than the horse's weak legs would carry him, and they leaped on his back. Their gnawing teeth bit into his flesh. The horse kicked and kicked. He rolled in the sand. Somehow he managed to shake the wolves off his back. He kicked at them madly and drove them off bleeding and wounded. For the moment he was

97

safe. But he knew he would not be safe very long, for other hungry beasts were roaming the desert.

" 'Alas! Alas!' the bleeding horse cried to himself. 'No bridle bit, no saddle rope, none of my master's battles ever gave me such wounds as the teeth of those hungry wolves. If only I were safe now in my master's camp! How happy I was there! Seldom was I hungry; not long was I thirsty. No journey of my master's ever made my legs as weak as they are now. I shall go to seek him!' "

"Did the horse find his master, oh my father?" Tamad asked.

"I was not there, my son, so how can I say? But since we cannot know with certainty, let us hope that the horse soon found his master's trail. Let us hope, too, that his master forgave him and took him back into his camp."

DON'T THROW STONES FROM
NOT YOURS TO YOURS
[*Israel*]

There was once a rich man with a large house surrounded by beautiful gardens. He had many servants, and he had them constantly working at beautifying his estate. As they worked in the gardens, they dug up many stones, and the rich man ordered them to fling the stones over the wall into the road. Every day it was this way. All the stones that the servants gathered they threw over the wall into the road where people walked.

One day the rich man was standing at this gate while his workmen were dumping stones this way. An old man of the nearby village was passing. He stopped and protested to the rich man.

"Why do you throw stones from not yours to yours?" he asked.

"What are you talking about?" the rich man said. "Don't you know that this great house and the grounds all around it are mine? My land extends to this very wall, and the road on the other side has nothing to do with me."

The old villager shook his head.

"God has been so good to you that you have lost the power to see that nothing in life is permanent," the villager said. And he went away, leaving the rich man to ponder on his words. But the rich man did not ponder long.

Soon he was walking among his workmen, encouraging them to clear more stones out of the garden and to fling them over the wall.

The years passed. The gardens were cleared of stones. And somehow the rich man's fortunes began to change. Little by little he lost his wealth. A time came when he had to sell a little of his precious gardens. Again he had to sell, and again. At last he gave up the house itself. He became shabby and poor. He was no better off than the most unfortunate and miserable of beggars.

Then one day, when he was old, he walked along the road past the great estate that had once been his. As he walked he stumbled among the stones that lay in his path. His feet were bare, and the stones cut them and bruised them.

He stopped and looked at the wall he remembered so well. And he sat at the roadside to rest his sore and tired feet. And then he recalled the words of the villager who had said long ago, "Why do you throw stones from not yours to yours?"

THE JUDGMENT OF KARAKOUSH
[*Egypt*]

The people have a proverb—"Like the Judgment of Karakoush"—which is heard whenever good laws are carried out in a silly or capricious way.

It is told that a thief once broke into a house to steal. He climbed the garden wall and came to a window which he tried to pry open. But the window frame was weak and gave way suddenly, and the thief fell into the house and broke his leg.

The next day, the thief, wobbling on his sound leg, appeared before Karakoush, the Governor. Showing his broken leg, he said:

"Your Excellency, I am a thief by profession. Yesterday I entered the house of a certain man, and as I was prying the window open it caved in, and I fell and broke my leg."

Karakoush shouted to the court guards to bring the owner of the house before him. Presently the owner of the house, trembling with fear and agitation, not knowing the nature of the charge against him, was dragged before the Governor. Karakoush repeated the accusation of the thief, and added:

"Why did you make your window so loose that it caved in and caused the thief to break his leg?"

What answer could the owner of the house make to such a charge? And since when had thieves the right of protection against honest people they tried to rob? But the man knew better than to argue with Karakoush. He thought for a moment, then he said to the Governor:

"Your Excellency, it was no fault of mine that the window of my house wasn't constructed right. I swear that I paid the carpenter sufficiently to make me a window strong enough to prevent such an accident."

"Bring the carpenter, then!" Karakoush commanded in a thundering voice.

And when the carpenter appeared, the Governor spoke sternly to him.

"This house owner asserts he paid you well to construct a strong window. Why then did you build a window so weak that this poor thief broke his leg when he tried to open it?"

The carpenter's face turned pale at this sudden and un-expected accusation. But he too knew how useless it was to argue with Karakoush, so after a little hesitation he said:

"Your Excellency, it wasn't my fault that the window frame wasn't fastened properly. I was driving a nail when a certain beautiful lady with a red dress passed under the window. I was distracted by the sight and drove the nail in crooked."

Karakoush demanded to know the name of the lady and instructed that she be brought before him at once.

When she appeared, the Governor repeated the charge of the carpenter, saying that if it hadn't been for her beauty and her red dress the carpenter wouldn't have been distracted, the window would have been stronger, and the thief wouldn't have fallen and broken his leg.

To this the lady answered with a smile.

"My beauty is from Allah, but my red dress is from the dyer. It was he who dyed it red and made me distract the carpenter."

"Then bring the dyer here," Karakoush ordered.

A few minutes later the dyer, too, stood trembling before the Governor.

"Oh, unscrupulous dabbler in dyes!" Karakoush roared. "Why did you dye this lady's dress red so that she attracted the attention of the carpenter, so that he drove the nail crooked and caused a weakness in the window frame, so that this thief broke his leg when he tried to pry it open?"

The poor dyer stood speechless and stunned with bewilderment. He stammered one excuse or another, but none appealed to the relentless Governor, who finally shouted out, "Take this fellow and hang him at the door of the prison!"

Now the dyer happened to be an extraordinarily tall fellow. When the soldiers took him to hang him at the door of the prison, they found that the door was too low, allowing no space for the rope. So they hurried back to the Governor and told him that they couldn't hang the dyer because he was too tall for the prison door.

But Karakoush, not to be daunted so easily, bellowed at the terrified soldiers.

"Go out and look for a short dyer and hang him in the place of this one!"

So the soldiers went out, as the Governor had commanded, and found a short dyer. They didn't listen to his wild protests that he had done no wrong, but dragged him to the prison door and hanged him.

Thus it is that when justice or reason gives way to silliness that hurts the innocent and leaves the guilty free, people say, "It is like the judgment of Karakoush."

AFRICA

THE FIRE ON THE MOUNTAIN
[*Ethiopia*]

People say that in the old days in the city of Addis Ababa there was a young man by the name of Arha. He had come as a boy from the country of Gurage, and in the city he became the servant of a rich merchant, Haptom Hasei.

Haptom Hasei was so rich that he owned everything that money could buy, and often he was very bored because he had tired of everything he knew, and there was nothing new for him to do.

One cold night, when the damp wind was blowing across the plateau, Haptom called to Arha to bring wood for the fire. When Arha was finished, Haptom began to talk.

"How much cold can a man stand?" he said, speaking at first to himself. "I wonder if it would be possible for a man to stand on the highest peak, Mount Intotto, where the coldest winds blow, through an entire night without blankets or clothing and yet not die?"

"I don't know," Arha said. "But wouldn't it be a foolish thing?"

"Perhaps, if he had nothing to gain by it, it would be a foolish thing to spend the night in that way," Haptom said. "But I would be willing to bet that a man couldn't do it."

"I am sure a courageous man could stand naked on Mount Intotto throughout an entire night and not die of it," Arha said. "But as for me, it isn't my affair since I've nothing to bet."

"Well, I'll tell you what," Haptom said. "Since you are so sure it can be done, I'll make a bet with you anyway. If you can stand among the rocks on Mount Intotto for an entire night without food or water or clothing or blankets or fire and not die of it, then I will give you ten acres of good farmland for your own, with a house and cattle."

Arha could hardly believe what he had heard.

"Do you really mean this?" he asked.

"I am a man of my word," Haptom replied.

"Then tomorrow night I will do it," Arha said, "and afterwards, for all the years to come, I shall till my own soil."

But he was very worried, because the wind swept bitterly across that peak. So in the morning Arha went to a wise old man of his own tribe and told him of the bet he had made. The old man listened quietly and thoughtfully, and when Arha had finished he said:

"I will help you. Across the valley from Intotto is a high rock which can be seen in the daytime. Tomorrow night, as the sun goes down, I shall build a fire there, so that it can be seen from where you stand on the peak. All night long you must watch the light of my fire. Do not close your eyes or let the darkness creep upon you. As you watch my fire, think of its warmth, and think of me, your friend, sitting there tending it for you. If you do this you will survive, no matter how bitter the night wind."

Arha thanked the old man warmly and went back to Haptom's house with a light heart. He told Haptom he was ready, and in the afternoon Haptom sent him, under the watchful eyes of other servants, to the top of Mount Intotto. There, as night fell, Arha removed his clothes and stood in the damp cold wind that swept across the plateau with the setting sun. Across the valley, several miles away, Arha saw the light of his friend's fire, which shone like a star in the blackness.

The wind turned colder and seemed to pass through his flesh and chill the marrow in his bones. The rock on which he stood felt like ice. Each hour the cold numbed him more, until he thought he would never be warm again, but he kept his eyes upon the twinkling light across the valley and remembered that his old friend sat there tending a fire for him. Sometimes wisps of fog blotted out the light, and then he strained to see until the fog passed. He sneezed and coughed and shivered and began to feel ill. Yet all night through he stood there, and only when the dawn came did he put on his clothes and go down the mountain back to Addis Ababa.

Haptom was very surprised to see Arha, and he questioned his servants thoroughly.

"Did he stay all night without food or drink or blankets or clothing?"

"Yes," his servants said. "He did all of these things."

"Well, you are a strong fellow," Haptom said to Arha. "How did you manage to do it?"

"I simply watched the light of a fire on a distant hill," Arha said.

"What! You watched a fire? Then you lose the bet, and you are still my servant, and you own no land!"

"But this fire was not close enough to warm me, it was far across the valley!"

"I won't give you the land," Haptom said. "You didn't fulfill the conditions. It was only the fire that saved you."

Arha was very sad. He went again to his old friend and told him what had happened.

"Take the matter to the judge," the old man advised him.

Arha went to the judge and complained, and the judge sent for Haptom. When Haptom told his story, and the servants said that Arha had watched a distant fire across the valley, the judge said, "No, you have lost, for Haptom Hasei's condition was that you must be without fire."

Once more Arha went to his old friend with the sad news that he was doomed to the life of a servant, as though he had not gone through the ordeal on the mountaintop.

"Don't give up hope," the old man said. "More wisdom grows wild in the hills than in any city judge."

He got up from where he sat and went to find a man named Hailu, in whose house he had been a servant when he was young. He explained to the good man about the bet between Haptom and Arha and asked if something couldn't be done.

"Don't worry about it," Hailu said after thinking for a while. "I will take care of it for you."

Some days later Hailu sent invitations to many people in the city to come to a feast at his house. Haptom was among them, and so was the judge who had ruled that Arha had lost the bet.

When the day of the feast arrived, the guests came riding on mules with fine trappings, their servants strung out behind them on foot. Haptom came with twenty servants, one of whom held a silk umbrella over his head to shade him from the sun, and four drummers played music that signified the great Haptom was here.

The guests sat on soft rugs laid out for them and talked. From the kitchen came the odors of wonderful things to eat: roast goat, roast corn and durra, pancakes called injera, and many tantalizing sauces. The smell of the food only accentuated the hunger of the guests. Time passed. The food should have been served, but they didn't see it, only smelled vapors that drifted from the kitchen. The evening came, and still no food was served. The guests began to whisper among themselves. It was very curious that the honorable Hailu had not had the food brought out. Still the smells came from the kitchen. At last one of the guests spoke out for all the others.

"Hailu, why do you do this to us? Why do you invite us to a feast and then serve us nothing?"

"Why, can't you smell the food?" Hailu asked with surprise.

"Indeed we can, but smelling is not eating; there is no nourishment in it!"

"And is there warmth in a fire so distant that it can hardly be seen?" Hailu asked. "If Arha was warmed by the fire he watched while standing on Mount Intotto, then you have been fed by the smells coming from my kitchen."

The people agreed with him; the judge now saw his mistake, and Haptom was shamed. He thanked Hailu for his advice, and announced that Arha was then and there the owner of the land, the house, and the cattle.

Then Hailu ordered the food brought in, and the feast began.

THE GHOST-BIRD
[*South Africa—A Zulu Tale*]

This is a legend about those small white birds that most
people call tickbirds. They are seen everywhere in the
South African veld, often sitting upon the backs of cattle
and other grazing animals. In marshy places, where the
tall reeds grow, the tickbirds build their nests by the hundreds. And sometimes, when the sun is setting, you can
see these birds flying slowly in its path—always searching.
Long ago they were known by another name—ghost-birds.
And this is how it happened.

In the old days the birds were not white, as they are now,
but red. They had red wings, red beaks, and red legs.
The first of these red birds appeared in the veld after a long
flight from another land. It had flown so far that it was
exhausted, and it fell from the sky almost dead with tiredness
and thirst.

It fell near the village of a Zulu boy named Indipi.
When Indipi saw the little red bird, he ran at once to the
spring for water. He filled a little jar with the cool water
and brought it back to where the red bird lay on the ground.
He opened the bird's beak, and drop by drop he let a little
of the water trickle into the poor, parched throat. Then
he placed the bird in the shade of a mimosa tree, and after
a while he brought some dried corn which he crushed into

meal. He held it in his hand, and the bird ate a little of it. Thus Indipi saved the red bird's life.

From that day on, the red bird and Indipi were close friends. Wherever the boy went, the bird followed. If Indipi happened to lose any of his playthings and was unable to find them, he would call the red bird, who would soar above the fields, looking this way and that way with his sharp eyes until it found the missing objects.

One day, when Indipi was walking in the fields, a deadly spider hung from a web in his path. Indipi didn't see it, but the sharp eyes of the red bird missed nothing. The bird plummeted from the air and snapped up the spider in its beak, saving Indipi's life.

In many ways the red bird rewarded Indipi for his kindness, and their friendship grew stronger and stronger.

But alas! Sad things were to happen in that part of the country where Indipi lived. A terrible drought fell on the land. Day after day, as the big hot sun burnt down on the country, the rivers and streams dried up. Even the reservoir behind the big mud dam dried up. The maize, once so straight and green, turned into withered stalks. The once fat oxen became thinner and thinner, and their bones showed through their skin. There was less and less corn to eat, and less and less water to drink. And still there was no sign of rain.

At last the headman of the village called the people together and said, "We must leave this place, the home of our ancestors, and find a new home where there is water to keep the people alive. Feed yourselves, then, on some of the corn that is left, but eat sparingly, for we must have food for the journey.   Of all the things we own, we will take only our cattle.   Everything else must be left behind.   My heart is sorrowful.   Carry out my commands."

The next day the people began their long journey. When Indipi's parents were ready, however, Indipi could not find his little red bird.   He searched and searched, but he couldn't find the bird anywhere.   He scanned the sky, but saw nothing.

"Come, come, Indipi," he mother urged, "the others are a long way ahead of us."

Indipi was heartbroken, but they could wait no longer. He joined his mother and the other women and children who were driving the oxen in front of them.   But while he walked, Indipi watched the sky, hoping for a sight of the little red bird, which never came.

What had happened to the bird was this: Seeing the distress of the people, he had set off on a long flight to look for water.   For many hours he flew, looking for a spring or a pond or a brook, but there was no water to be seen. So, planning to make another flight later, he returned to the village.   But when he arrived there he found the village deserted.   There wasn't a scrap of corn left, nor a drop of water to drink.   Weary and thirsty from his long flight, the red bird lay down and died.

But a strange thing happened.   The next morning when the sun came up, a pure white bird arose from the spot where the red bird had died.   This ghost-bird soared into the sky and began to search for Indipi's people.   After flying for some time, it saw some oxen below, and swooping down it was soon among them.

Standing on the back of one of the oxen, the ghost-bird asked if they had seen Indipi. "The people left us behind because they had no water," the cattle said. "Travel in the direction of the setting sun and you will find them."

The ghost-bird flew on, in the direction of the setting sun, and whenever he saw cattle on the veld he came down and asked for news of Indipi and his people. Always he received the same answer. "Fly toward the setting sun."

At last, however, he saw no more cattle. He flew on and on, trying first one direction, then another, but the people of the village were not to be found.

To this very day, the ghost-birds fly to earth whenever they see cattle. They perch themselves on the backs of the oxen and ask the same question, "Where is Indipi?" And always the answer is the same, "We do not know, he disappeared in the west."

But the ghost-birds never give up. They go on and on, forever searching for Indipi in the path of the setting sun.

HOW PAKAYANA THE SPIDER GOT HIS SMALL WAIST

[*Liberia*]

Once in the old days there were two neighboring villages, Kemojav and Momojav, which prided themselves on the great festivals they held each year. The festivities in Kemojav took place at the same time as the festivities in Momojav. From the surrounding countryside, some people went to one village for the celebration and some went to the other. It came about that a great rivalry grew up between Momojav and Kemojav. Each one tried to outdo the other with its festival. On the last day of the celebration, there was always a great feast, and the visitors were invited to eat as much as they wanted.

Pakayana the spider was a famous eater. He was always hungry. Whenever he saw food he ate it. And never did he eat so much as at the annual feasts in Kemojav and Momojov. Sometimes he would go to one village and eat, sometimes to the other. But even after glutting himself he was still hungry.

One year Pakayana decided that only if he ate both at the Kemojav feast and the Momojav feast would he get enough to satisfy him. But the villages were some distance apart, and it took time to get from one to the other. And one never knew exactly when the eating would begin.

So he contrived a plan which would permit him to eat

at both villages. He hired two men to help him, and he bought enough rope to stretch from Kemojav to Momojav, and cut it into two lengths. He tied one of the ropes around his waist and gave the end to one man. He tied the other rope around his waist and gave the end to the other man. Then he instructed them this way: One of them was to go to Kemojav, the other was to go to Momojav. When the eating started in Momojav, the man who was there was to pull on his rope. When the eating began in Kemojav, the man stationed there was to pull on his rope. That way, Pakayana would know which village was eating first. He would go there and eat his fill, then hurry to the other village to continue his eating.

So one man went to Kemojav with his rope, and the other to Momojav with his rope, and Pakayana stood halfway between the two villages. Pakayana was very satisfied with himself. As he waited he couldn't help but think of the rice, goat meat, beef, and chicken that were being prepared at the festivals.

Time went by, and Pakayana waited. He became irritable and angry that the signal didn't come from one direction or the other. At last, however, something happened. The feast began in Momojav. And at precisely the same moment the feast began in Kemojav. The two men whom Pakayana had hired began to pull on their ropes. They were very strong men, and they tugged very hard. They pulled so hard that Pakayana couldn't move in one direction or another. He just bobbed up and down in one place. The two men were stubborn and persistent as well as strong. They kept pulling and pulling. The ropes around Pakayana's waist were getting tighter and tighter. For a long time in Momojav and Kemojav the people ate. Finally they were finished. Only then did the two men stop pulling. They went back to where they had left Pakayana, and they found him there lying on the ground moaning and gasping for breath. They took the ropes off him. But where the ropes had squeezed him around the middle, Pakayana was now very thin, with half of his body swelled out above and half swelled out below.

And thus Pakayana remains to this day with a tiny waist. Whenever people see it, they remember the time Pakayana tried to eat at the feasts of Momojav and Kemojav at the same time.

EUROPE

THE SON OF THE HUNTER
[*Greece*]

There was once a hunter who had a son. When the hunter was about to die, he told his wife, "Hunting is a hard life. Let my son find a different profession for himself." The hunter died, time passed, and the boy grew into a young man.

One day he said to his mother, "Where is my father's gun?"

The mother replied, "It was your father's wish that you be something else but a hunter."

The young man asked, "Wasn't hunting good enough for my father?" And he took his father's gun and went out in the woods. He wandered around until he found a deer. He shot it, and, putting it on his shoulders, he carried it to the city market place. While he was trying to sell it, the King's minister came along and said, "How much will you charge for your deer?"

The hunter's son replied, "How much will you offer me?"

The King's minister answered, "Ten piastres."

The hunter's son said, "That is not enough." And he refused to sell.

The King's minister became angry, and determined that he would make the young man sell the deer for even less. So he went to the King, saying, "There is a man in the city selling a deer.   It is a good one, fit for your table.   But you must not offer more than a piastre and a half for it."

The King sent for the hunter's son, and he came with the deer.

"How much are you asking for the deer?" the King asked him.

"Surely, you will know a fair price," the young man said.

"A fair price is a piastre and a half," the King declared.

One does not argue with a king.   The hunter's son took the piastre and a half and went away.

The next day the King sent for the hunter's son again. This time he said, "I wish to have for myself a palace of ivory.   You are a hunter, and you are the man to find the elephants and get the ivory for me.   When you have brought the ivory, you will build my palace."

The hunter's son was silent.   The King asked him, "Why are you silent?   If you can do it, say so.   If you can't do it, say so.   But if you fail, you will be executed."

The hunter's son said, "Yes, I can do it."

But he went away discouraged, for who was he to find enough ivory to build a palace?   He went to his house and told his mother: "I am not long for this world.   The King has commanded me to bring him ivory and build him a palace.   As I certainly can't do it, he will kill me."   He told her what had happened, and said, "Give me a knapsack with a little bread, for I must go away where I can't be found."

The young man's mother told him, "I remember well what your father used to say: 'Up there on the great mountain the elephants come once each week to drink in the fresh-water pond.   If the King would give me a little help, I would get all the ivory of their tusks.   I would drain off the pond and fill it up with wine.   Then when the elephants come they would drink the wine and get drunk, and I would be able to take their ivory.' "

When the young man heard this he was encouraged.   He went back to the King and said, "I am ready to get the ivory. Give me forty barrels of wine and men to work with me, and I will begin."

The King gave him the wine and the men.   The men carried the wine, and the hunter's son took them all to the great mountain.   He drained the pond on the mountain and filled it with wine, and then he took his men into the woods and hid.   When the elephants came, they went to the pond and drank.   The wine made them drunk.   Some of them staggered around helplessly.   Others fell down and slept. They could not defend themselves.   The hunter's son and his men came out of the woods and cut off the elephants' ivory tusks and carried them back to the city, where they built an ivory palace for the King.

When the King's minister, who had caused so much trouble, saw what had been done, he grew angry again.   He went to the King, determined this time to get rid of the hunter's son.   He said to the King, "There is a distant mountain in the north, where seven brothers live.   The seven brothers have a beautiful sister who should be your wife and live in your new ivory palace.   Send the hunter's son to get her."

The King thought about this, and it seemed very desirable. So he sent for the hunter's son and commanded him to go to the distant mountain in the north and bring the girl who lived there with her seven brothers.

In great despair, the young man took his knapsack and began his journey, not knowing whether he would ever return.   He traveled far, and one day he came to a wide river. Sitting on the bank of the river was a man who was drinking and drinking, and as he drank he kept saying, "I am thirsty! I am thirsty!   Never do I get enough water!"   The wide river flowed swiftly, and as fast as it came along the man drank it.

The young man said, "What kind of a person are you, that you are always thirsty?"

"Yes, I am always thirsty," the man replied.   "And I am miserable because I travel alone.   If I had a companion I wouldn't be miserable."

"Let us be companions," the son of the hunter said.   And so they traveled together.

As they walked toward the north, they encountered another man, huddling before a huge fire.   He was repeating over and over again, "I am cold!   I am cold!   Never is there enough heat anywhere!"   The son of the hunter took him also as a companion, and they continued the journey toward the north.

On the way they met a man who was gulping down great quantities of food.   Plate after plate he filled and ate, saying all the while, "I am hungry!   I am hungry!"   The son of the hunter took this man too as a companion, and the four travelers went on together.

As they traveled, they saw a man with his ear to the ground, listening to all that was happening in the world.

They took him also and now there were five of them in all.

They came then upon a man who was a great jumper. He held big stones in his hands, and he would throw the stones behind him and leap forward at the same time. The way in which he used the stones, throwing them backward while he went forward, made him jump incredible distances. The son of the hunter took him as a companion, and now there were six.

They met still one more man as they journeyed, and he could make the earth shake and rumble. The hunter's son took him too, and now there were seven in all. The seven companions came together to the great mountain where the seven brothers lived. When the seven brothers saw them, they rushed forward to destroy them. But seeing that the seven companions were strong young men, the seven brothers hesitated, and asked, "Why are you here and what do you want?"

The son of the hunter answered, "We have come for your sister; the King wants her for a wife, and she will live in the new ivory palace."

The seven brothers went back to their house and made a plan. The son of the hunter asked, "What are they saying?" And the man who could put his ear to the ground and hear everything listened.

Then he said, "They say they will give us seven huge cauldrons of food. If we can eat it all, they will give us their sister. If we can't do it, they will refuse."

"How can we manage it?" the hunter's son inquired.

"Ha, what are you thinking?" the man who was always hungry answered. "Am I not here?"

The seven brothers took the companions into the house and placed the seven great cauldrons of food before them. Six of the companions soon could eat no more, but the one who was always hungry threw his spoon away and ate directly from his cauldron. When his own cauldron was empty, he went to the next one, then the next, and the next, until all of the food was gone.

But the seven brothers had no intention of letting their sister go, and they thought up more tests for the seven companions. They brought seven great jars of water for the companions to drink. Now the man who was always thirsty took the jars and drank them dry. When he was finished, he complained, "Bring me something to drink, I am thirsty."

So the seven brothers thought of another obstacle to put in the way of the companions. They said, "One of you must endure the fiery heat of our steam bath before we give up our sister."

And the man who was always cold said, "Please, let me do it. I can't stand this northern climate."

He went into the fiery heat of the steam bath. The brothers made it so hot that a man would die of it. They waited. There was no sound from the steam bath. They opened the door and looked inside, and the man shouted, "Close the door! You are letting cold air in here!"

The companions brought him out of the steam bath then, and the seven brothers said to them: "Oh you men, whatever we have asked you to do you have done. But there is one thing more. If you can do it, we will let you have our sister. On the next mountain there is a spring. One of you must go and bring some water from it. Our sister too will go and bring some of it. If you can bring it first, you can have our sister. If our sister brings it first, you cannot have her."

Then the man who could jump took two heavy stones in his hands and flung them backward, while he went forward in a mighty leap, all the way to the next mountain. He filled a bottle with water and began to return leisurely. On the way, he met the girl who was still on her way to the spring. He said to her, "As you see, we have won. So let us sit awhile and talk." So they sat and talked, but the great jumper fell asleep. The girl emptied the water from his bottle into hers and started home.

The son of the hunter began to wonder what had happened to the great jumper. The man who could hear everything put his ear to the ground and said, "We are losing. He has fallen asleep, and the girl has taken his water and is returning."

But the companion who could make the earth shake said, "I will awaken him."

He made the earth quake and rumble, and the great jumper awoke and saw that the girl had taken the water and gone. He made another great leap and come to where she was running. He took the water back from her, and with another jump arrived at where his companions were waiting.

Now, as everything had been done by the companions successfully, the brothers could think of no more tests, and they gave their sister to the hunter's son and his companions. So the hunter's son returned with his friends to the King.

The King was very pleased when he saw the beautiful

girl.   The King's minister was angry when he saw that the son of the hunter had been successful.

As for the girl, she looked at the King, she looked at the King's minister, and she looked at the ivory palace.   She asked, "Who brought the ivory for this palace?"

The King replied, "The son of the hunter."

"And who built the palace?"

"The son of the hunter."

"And who made the journey and took me from the northern mountain?"

"The son of the hunter."

"Since the son of the hunter did everything," the girl said, "why should I marry you?"

Then she declared, "May your minister be changed into a mouse because of his bad behavior, and may the King be turned into a cat and chase the mouse."

And thus it happened.   The minister became a mouse, and the King became a cat, and he chased the mouse.

The people took the son of the hunter for their new king. The son of the hunter took the girl for his wife.   And they lived together in the ivory palace.

KING SVATOPLUK AND
THE THREE STICKS
[*Czechoslovakia*]

Thirteen centuries ago the kingdoms of Moravia, Bohemia, and Slovakia were united under the rule of King Svatopluk, the founder of the Greater Moravian Empire. King Svatopluk governed with a strong hand, a stubborn will, and a wise head, and successfully defended his Empire against enemies who wished to conquer it.

But a time came when Svatopluk grew old and sick, and he worried about the future of his country. One day the King sent for his three sons, and they came to his bedside. He said to them, "My sons, my strength is failing. I fear that I may not live very long. And so I have sent for you to say what is in my mind. I have worked long and hard to build this great Empire. Soon it is you who will have the responsibility of defending it and keeping it united. We have enemies with unending ambition to destroy it. I implore you to protect our Empire."

Svatopluk was silent then for a moment. He motioned for a servant to come to his bedside and spoke to him in a low voice. The servant went out of the room, while Svatopluk's three sons stood and wondered. In a few minutes the servant returned with three long flexible sticks, which he placed in the hands of the King. The three sons looked at the sticks uncertainly, for it was with such sticks that

Svatopluk had sometimes chastized them when they were younger. King Svatopluk smiled.

"I see you are familiar with these objects," he said. "As you may observe, they are thin and can be bent easily by the pressure of the hands."

He then gave the sticks back to the servant and instructed him to bind them together. The servant bound them around and around with a cord, until they resembled one single stick instead of three.

"I fear for you, my sons," the King continued. "You quarrel among yourselves. If you continue to live this way, you will lose the lands that are your inheritance. Only if you are united will our Empire survive."

Svatopluk took the bundle of sticks from his servant and handed it to his sons. He said, "I want you each, in turn, to try to break this bundle of sticks."

So each son, in his turn, took the sticks and tried to break them. Not only did they fail to break them, they found it almost impossible to make the sticks bend.

"This is the lesson of unity," the King said. "If you remain bound together in peace and common purpose, you will be strong and invincible."

He then ordered the servant to unbind the sticks and give one to each of the sons. The young men took their individual sticks, and the King said, "Now let me see you break the sticks you hold in your hands."

Each of the sons broke his stick in two without any difficulty.

"This is the lesson of disunity," Svatopluk explained. "If you do not work together, you will be weak and will be broken. This is my last warning to you. Live together in harmony and common purpose, and no power will be strong enough to defeat you. Face your foes together with courage, determination, and fearlessness. Govern with justice, mercy, and charity. Then neither corruption from within nor attacks from without can break your strong alliance."

This was King Svatopluk's advice to his sons. It was not many days after that he died.

But they soon forgot their father's advice. They found it impossible to agree among themselves. They continued to quarrel, and one by one they were conquered and broken. Invaders came from the East and the West, split up the Empire, and ruled over the people.

Thus King Svatopluk's Great Moravian Empire came to an end. Had Svatopluk's sons remained bound together in unity, the history of Europe would have been different. But each of them, going his own way, proved weak and helpless before their common enemies.

THE BEST WISH

[*Yugoslavia*]

Three brothers once possessed a pear tree and took turns guarding it. While two of them went to work, the third stayed at home to watch the tree and make sure that no harm came to it and that no one stole the pears.

An angel was sent down from heaven to test the hearts of the three brothers. Taking the form of a beggar, he approached the pear tree on a day when the oldest brother was guarding it. He held out his hand and said, "In heaven's name, brother, give me a ripe pear."

The oldest brother handed him a pear immediately. "I can give you this one," he said, "because it is mine, but none of the others because they belong to my brothers."

The angel thanked him and went away.

The next day the second brother was on guard, and the angel returned as a beggar and again begged the charity of a ripe pear.

"Take this one," answered the second brother. "It belongs to me, but I can't give you any of the others because they belong to my brothers."

The angel thanked the second brother and departed.

The third day, when he approached the youngest brother, the boy replied in the same manner.

On the following day the angel, disguised as a monk, came early to the brothers' house while they were all still at home.

"Come with me, my sons," he said, "and perhaps I can find you something better to do than to guard a single pear tree."

The brothers went with him, and they walked for a long time until they came to the banks of a broad, deep river.

The angel spoke to the oldest brother. "My son, if I were to grant you one wish, what would you ask?"

"It would be wonderful," said the oldest brother, "if all this water were turned into wine and belonged to me!"

The angel lifted his staff and made the sign of the cross, and at once the broad river became wine from great wine presses. Men were filling a large number of casks and rolling them about. A huge industry appeared, with shed, storehouses, wagons, and men running back and forth busily and addressing the oldest brother respectfully as Master.

"You have your wish," said the angel. "But do not forget God's poor, now that you are rich."

They left the oldest brother busy with his wine and traveled on until they came to a great field where flocks of pigeons were feeding.

"If I were to grant you one wish," said the angel to the second brother, "what would you ask for?"

"It would be marvelous," replied the second brother, "if all the pigeons in this field were turned into sheep and belonged to me!"

The angel lifted his staff, made the sign of the cross, and immediately the field was covered with sheep. And there were sheds and houses; women were milking the ewes and skimming the milk and making cheeses. There were men preparing meat for the market, and other men cleaning wool.

All of them, as they hurried up and down, respectfully called the second brother Master.

"There is your wish," said the angel. "But now that you are prosperous, do not forget God's poor."

Then he and the youngest brother journeyed on.

"Now, my son," said the angel, "you may make one wish, too."

The youngest brother said quietly, "There's only one thing I pray heaven for, Father. And that is a truly pious wife."

"My son, you have asked for the hardest thing of all!" cried the angel. "There are only three pious women in the world, and two of them are already married. The third is a princess who at this very moment is being sought in marriage by two kings. However, let us go to the King and present your request."

So they trudged along to the city where the Princess lived and entered the palace, looking shabby and stained by travel.

The King granted them an audience, and when they told their mission he exclaimed, "How can I decide? Two kings and now this youth all ask for my daughter's hand the same day! What shall I do?"

"Let heaven decide," said the angel.

"Of course," replied the King. "But how?"

"In this manner. Cut three branches of grapevine, and let the Princess mark each branch with the name of a different suitor. Then let her plant the three branches in the garden tonight. Tomorrow you must give her in marriage to the man whose branch has blossomed during the night and by morning is covered with ripe clusters of grapes."

"That is an excellent idea," declared the King.

The Princess and the suitors agreed to it; the Princess named and planted the three branches. In the morning, two of the branches were withered and bare, but the third was covered with green leaves and ripe clusters of grapes, and the name on the blossoming branch was that of the youngest brother. The King accepted heaven's ruling without question, led his daughter to the church, and had her married to the strange young man. Then he sent them off with his blessing, and the angel led the young couple to a forest and left them there.

After a year had passed, the angel was sent back to earth to see how the three brothers were getting along. Again assuming the garments of a beggar, he went to the oldest brother, who was busy among his vines and his wine presses.

"Please give a poor man a cup of wine," begged the angel.

"Get out, you old rascal!" shouted the oldest brother in a rage. "If I gave a cup of wine to every beggar who came along, I'd soon be a beggar myself. Off with you!"

The angel lifted his staff, made the sign of the cross, and behold! The wine and the presses and the shed and the workers disappeared, and the broad, deep river flowed again in that place.

"In your prosperity you have forgotten God's poor," said the angel severely. "Go back to your pear tree!"

And he went on to find the second brother, who was busy in his dairy.

"Pray give a poor man a morsel of cheese," begged the angel.

"Be off with you, or I'll call the dogs!" shouted the second

134

brother. "I'll give no cheese to a lazy good-for-nothing!"

The angel lifted his staff and made the sign of the cross. And the sheep and the dairy and all the busy laborers vanished, and instead there was only a field where flocks of pigeons were feeding.

"You have forgotten God's poor," said the angel sternly. "Go back to your pear tree!"

Then the angel hurried on to the forest where he had left the youngest brother and his wife, the Princess. And he found them living in great poverty in a little hut.

"God be with you!" said the angel, still disguised as an old beggar. "In heaven's name, give me a little supper and shelter for the night."

"We are very poor ourselves, but come in," said the youngest brother. "You are welcome to share what we have."

The youngest brother and the Princess made the old beggar comfortable by the fire, and the wife set three places for the evening meal. They were so poor that the loaf baking in the oven was not made of flour at all but of pounded bark which the youngest brother had gathered from the trees.

"I am ashamed," murmured the wife, "that we have no real bread to offer you, our guest."

"I really need very little," answered the angel, smiling.

But when she opened the oven, there was a browned loaf of wheaten bread, and she cried, "God be praised!" and wept with surprise and delight.

She drew a pitcher of water at the spring, but when she began pouring it into the cups it had changed into sweet wine. And the youngest brother was as overjoyed as she.

The angel said, "In your happiness, you have not forgotten God's poor, and God will reward you!"

He raised his staff, made the sign of the cross, and the poor little hut disappeared. In its place arose a marvelous palace filled with riches and beautiful things. Many servants passed to and fro and addressed the younger brother as "my lord" and his wife as "my lady."

And the old beggar arose with a smile and blessed them. "God gives you these riches," he said, "and they will be yours as long as you share them with others. Bless you and farewell, my children!"

And the angel returned to heaven to report on the goodness of the youngest brother's heart, while the youngest brother and his dear wife lived in great honor and love.

THE OLD FATHER
WHO WENT TO SCHOOL
[*Ukrainian S.S.R.*]

There was once an old man with four sons. He lived to a great age, and a time came when he divided all his goods among them. "I will pass my remaining days among my children," he thought.

So the old man went to live with his oldest son. At first the oldest son treated his father with reverence. "It is only right and proper that we should give food and shelter to our father," he said. "We should care for him and clothe him." So it was for a time. The oldest son was a good son to his father. But after a while he began to regret his hospitality and was rough to his father and sometimes even shouted at him.

The old man no longer had his own place in the house as in the beginning. His clothes went unmended, and no one cut his food for him. The oldest son regretted that he had undertaken to care for the old man and began to resent every morsel of bread that his father ate.

At last there was no choice for the old man. He left the house and went to his second son. But he soon discovered that he had only exchanged wheat for straw. Whenever he began to eat, his son and daughter-in-law looked sour and muttered something disagreeable between their teeth. The woman scolded the old man constantly, saying, "It was hard enough for us to make both ends meet before you came. And now we have to keep an old man in the bargain." The old father soon had enough of this, and he went to his third son. There it was the same, and he moved on to his youngest son. His youngest son was no different from the others. The old man moved from the house of one to the house of the other, and he was glad to leave them all. Each one of the sons threw the burden of keeping their father on one of the others. There were great arguments among them as to who should take the responsibility. One had one good excuse, and another had another, and so none of them would keep him. This one had a lot of little children, that one had a scold for a wife, this house was too small, that one was too poor. "Go where you will, old man," they said, "only don't come to us."

And the old man wept before his children and didn't know which way to turn. He struggled no more, but let them do with him as they wished.

So all four sons met to decide what to do. At last they agreed among themselves that the best thing the old man could do would be to go away to school somewhere. "There will be a bench for him to sit on there," they said, "and he can take something to eat in his knapsack." They told the old man about it. But the old man didn't want to go to school. He begged his children not to send him there, and he wept again.

"My eyes are growing dim," he said. "I can hardly see the bright world around me. How then can I see the tiny black print in a book? Moreover, I have never learned my letters in all my long life. How can I begin now? How can a clerk be made out of an old man on the point of death?"

But there was no use talking. His children had decided that he would have to go to school, and they sent him on his way.

As he passed through the forest on the way to the next town, he met a nobleman driving along in a carriage. The old man stepped aside to let the carriage pass and stood respectfully at the edge of the road. But the nobleman stopped his horses and got out of the carriage. He asked the old man where he was going.

"To school," the old man replied.

"To school, Old Father? Surely at your age you should be resting at ease in your house."

So the old man spoke of his misery, tears running down his face. When the nobleman heard the story, he was full of compassion. He thought for a while, and then he said, "Well, Old Father, it is certain that school is not the place for you. Weep no more, and do not let your soul be troubled. I will help you."

He took from his belt a silk purse, the kind that only the richest man would carry. And he poured something into the purse until it was almost full to the brim. He tied it closed, and he placed it in a wooden box from his carriage.

"Take this home," he said, "and tell your children these words." The nobleman instructed the old man what to say. The old man thanked him with deep gratitude and went back the way he had come. When he returned to his children, they saw him carrying the box under his arm. When one carries a heavy box, there is always something in it.

The old man's sons and their wives didn't protest this time. They rushed out to meet him to find out what treasure he was bringing back from the forest. Some of them even said, "Come and rest, father, you must be tired," or "Eat, father, you must be hungry."

Then the old man told his tale, as instructed by his chance friend in the forest. "My dear children," he began. "Long, long ago, when I was young and knocked about in the world a bit, I made a little money. I thought I would save it for the future, for of course a person never knows what will happen. So I went into the forest and dug a hole under an oak tree, and there I hid my little store of money. I didn't bother about the money afterwards, because I had such good children. But when you sent me to school I passed by this very same oak tree, and I said to myself, 'I wonder if these few silver pieces have been waiting for their owner all this time!' So I dug and found them, and I have brought them home. I shall keep them until I die. But after my death, whoever shall have been found to cherish me the most, whoever has given me the kindest treatment, he shall be given the greater part of what is in this box. So now, dear children, receive me back. Which of you will be kind to your old father—for money?"

Then the brothers fell all over each other being kind to the old man. One said, "Live in my house!" Another said, "No, in my house!" They fed him well and tended his clothes and were solicitous for his welfare.

And this is the way it remained until, at last, the old man died.

Then the sons made haste to get hold of the box and

began to argue about who had been kindest and deserved the largest share of what was in it. People of the village were called upon to judge the matter. At last it was agreed that all four sons had been equally kind to their father since he returned from the forest, and that they should share the legacy equally.

The sons gave their father a magnificent funeral and made a tremendous banquet for the mourners in the village. The sons contributed money to the church and asked the priest to say forty days of prayers. Each trying to outdo the other, they gave more money gifts to the church to pay for a requiem.

And when the ceremonies were over they hastened to the box to open it. They found within it a magnificent silk purse. They shook it, and it tinkled deliciously. Then they untied the purse and emptied its contents out on the table. They could not believe their eyes. It was nothing but bits of glass!

When it dawned on the brothers that the treasure was worthless, they became angry and began to argue. But the people of the village began to laugh.

"See what you have gained by sending your helpless old father to school!" they said. "He was a long time in getting his learning. But what he learned, he learned well!"

THE KING AND THE PEASANT
[*Poland*]

The sun was setting, and an aged peasant named Matthew was just ending his day of plowing in the fields. In the distance he heard a song echoing between the hills. Turning in the direction of the sound, he saw a large company of men on horseback come out of the forest and ride along the highway toward the village. It was the King and his nobles returning from the hunt. The King rode at the head of the company, followed by his lords and counselors and many others in gleaming armor, to the accompaniment of singing and the blowing of horns.

It was a magnificent sight, and Matthew, when he saw the knights in their shining armor, could not take his eyes off them. Great was his astonishment when the King, bringing his company to a halt on the highway by a signal with his hand, rode with three of his counselors directly across the field to where Matthew stood. The old peasant pulled up his belt, smoothed out his coat, and, holding his cap in his hand, humbly awaited the approach of the King.

The King rode right up to the bowing peasant and, having greeted him in God's name, said, "Old man, you did not rise early enough to do your work."

Matthew replied, "I did, my gracious and beloved King, but the Lord God did not allow me."

The King then asked, "Grandfather, how long has that

snowy orchard been blooming on yonder sage mountain top?"

"Forty years already, my gracious Lord."

The King, nodding his head in understanding, asked again, "How long have the streams been flowing from under the mountain?"

"Oh," Matthew replied, "for more than fifteen years, my Lord, they have been flowing and flowing."

"So far, so good," said the King. "Now tell me: when three foolish geese from the East come to you, will you be able to fleece them?"

"Oh, very well, my beloved and gracious King," the old peasant readily replied.

Upon hearing these words, the King gave a golden belt to Matthew and took leave of him with God's blessing. Joining his company, together with his three counselors, he was soon lost behind clouds of dust on the way to the capital.

When they arrived at their destination, the King, his counselors, and the knights sat down to a sumptuous meal. And when they had finished, the King asked his three counselors who had accompanied him on the visit to the peasant to explain what his questions and the peasant's replies had meant.

The counselors thought and thought for a long time, trying to explain the riddles, but none of their guesses satisfied the King. At last the King said they could have thirty days to find the right answers. But if they failed, the King said, he would choose other counselors to replace them.

Night after night the counselors pondered and deliberated, but they could not unravel the meaning of the words. In the end they went to see the peasant Matthew.

Old Matthew received them at the threshold of his cottage, bowing humbly, but he refused to enlighten them. The counselors pleaded with him and threatened him, but it was all useless. Only when they had put on the table a hundred golden ducats each did Matthew, having gathered all the money into his pocket, spell out the meaning of the riddles for them.

"My first answer to our gracious King meant that I married young and had children, but that the Lord God took them away from me.

"The second answer meant that forty years ago my hair turned gray.

"Then the King asked how long the streams had been flowing, meaning my tears of grief.

"Finally, the three foolish geese from the East referred to you, my lords, who came here to pay me to explain the conversation between the King and me. And as I promised the King, the geese have been well fleeced."

THE SOLDIER AND THE KNAPSACK

[*Byelorussian S.S.R.*]

It happened that a soldier who had ended his long service in the army of the King was walking along a road. As he walked he thought, "For twenty-five years I served the King. And during all those years I was never in need of food or clothing, nor did I ever lack a horse. But now that my service has come to an end, my pockets are empty, and I suffer from the cold wind; I have no horse to carry me, and, as for food, I have nothing in the world but three loaves of bread."

While the soldier was thinking of the sudden change of his fortune, an aged beggar approached him and asked for alms. The soldier took one of the three loaves of bread which he carried and gave it to the beggar, who said, "May God bless you for this."

The soldier continued on his way, and before long a second aged beggar came to him and asked for something to eat. He gave his second loaf of bread away, and the beggar blessed him for his generosity.

And when he had walked a few miles a third beggar came and humbly asked for help. The soldier took out his last loaf of bread, thinking he would break it in half and share it. But then he thought, "Suppose this unfortunate man should meet the other two. They might say, 'See, we have a whole loaf each, while you have only a half!'" And so the soldier gave the beggar the third loaf.

The beggar said, "God will reward you for your goodness, soldier, and perhaps even I can help you a little if you can tell me what you need."

"Your blessing is reward enough," the soldier replied.

"Don't be misled by appearances," the beggar said.

He took a pack of cards from inside his cloak and gave them to the soldier. "If you play with these cards, you cannot lose even though you play against the greatest of gamblers." And he also took the knapsack which he carried and put it in the soldier's hand. "If you see anything that you want—bird, beast, or any living creature—cry out, 'Enter my knapsack,' and he will enter it and become your property."

The soldier thanked the beggar and went his way. He came soon to the edge of a lake, and seeing three wild geese flying over the water he said to himself, "Now I will test the knapsack." He opened it and called out, "Enter my knapsack, you three geese over the lake!" And the three geese turned and flew to him and went into the knapsack one by one. He closed the knapsack and tied it and went on until he reached the city. He found an inn, and he said to the innkeeper, "Here are three geese. Cook the first one for my dinner. For the second one, give me vodka to drink. And the third is yours."

The innkeeper agreed, and as the soldier ate he looked from the window of the inn and saw the ruins of a large palace. The walls were crumbling, and the grounds were overgrown with weeds and brambles. The soldier asked the innkeeper, "What is this desolation?"

And the innkeeper replied, "It is the palace of the Prince who rules this city, but for seven years it has been haunted. There are no tenants in it, except the demons of the underworld. Each night the demons meet there to feast, dance, and drink until dawn. Many brave men have attempted to drive the demons away, but their efforts ended in failure."

When the soldier heard this he went to the Prince of the city and asked permission to spend a single night within the palace to deal with the demons. The Prince refused, saying, "You are brave, soldier, but I must refuse. For there were others before you who tried to clear the demons out, but all of them failed, and none returned alive."

Yet the soldier persisted until at last the Prince gave in, saying, "Go then, since you wish it, and God be with you." Then the soldier went into the palace and found the hall of state, and he sat on the Prince's throne and lighted his pipe and smoked contentedly.

When the church bells rang the hour of midnight, the demons appeared. Where there had been only silence before, now there was shouting and screaming as the demons played. The great hall of state was crowded with them from wall to wall. They ate, danced, and drank wildly, and so intent were they on what they were doing that they didn't immediately notice the soldier sitting there on the Prince's throne. When at last they saw him they asked in surprise, "Ha there, soldier! Are you here to join in our revels? Will you drink, dance, or gamble for money?"

"I will gamble with you for money," the soldier said, taking out the pack of cards given to him by the beggar.

And he gambled with the demons. As the hours went by, he won their silver, bit by bit, until at last the demons cried out, "He has won all our silver!" But the chief demon ordered, "Then let us play for gold!" And he sent messengers to bring the gold from the storehouse, and the game went on, until at last the gold as well as the silver lay in a pile beside the soldier. When the demons cried out in anguish that their gold was gone, their chief commanded, "Seize this intruder! Eat him and scatter his bones!"

"Is that the way it is to be?" the soldier asked. "Let us see!" And he opened his knapsack and said, "Enter my knapsack, you demons of the underworld!"

And when they heard this, they could not keep from entering. One by one they leaped into the knapsack, struggling but helpless. And though the knapsack was small, at last there were thousands of demons in it, and when the last one had entered, the soldier tightened the cord and hung the knapsack on the wall.

Where the wild revels had been going on there was now only silence, and the soldier lay down and slept. And when the Prince's servants came in the morning, expecting to find only bones, they found the soldier sleeping peacefully. They woke him, and he told them the story.

Then the soldier sent for blacksmiths with heavy sledges. They put the knapsack on an anvil and pounded it with the sledges until the demons inside cried for mercy.

"Have pity, soldier! Forever we will hold your name in

dread! We will go away from this palace and never set foot here again!"

So the soldier stopped the blacksmiths and opened the knapsack. The demons came out and fled to the underworld from which they had come. As the last demon came out of the knapsack, the soldier caught him by the leg, saying, "Promise that you will serve me whenever I need you." And the demon replied, "Yes, yes, I promise!" And when the soldier let him go, he fled after his fellow demons.

Then the soldier went to the Prince of the city, bringing the gold and silver with him, and described all that had happened. The Prince took the soldier into his house as one of the family, saying "You shall live with me as a brother."

So the soldier stayed there, the gifts of the beggar having brought him the best of fortune, and he took a wife and in the course of time he had a son.

But it happened that the soldier's child became sick, and they could find no medicine to cure him. The soldier racked his brains thinking what he might do to save his son. And then he thought of the demon who had promised to aid him. So he called out, "Oh demon who pledged me aid, I need you!"

The demon kept his promise and came. In an instant he was standing there, saying, "What do you want of me?"

"Here lies my only son, with a sickness we don't know how to cure," the soldier said. "Heal him."

The demon took a drinking glass from under his clothing and filled it with clear water. He said to the soldier, "Look in the glass now and tell me what you see."

The soldier looked in the glass of water, and he saw Death standing at his son's feet. He told the demon what he saw and was grieved, but the demon replied, "Do not grieve, for your son's health will be restored. But if Death stood at the head of the bed instead of the foot, no power in the world could save him."

The demon then sprinkled the water over the child and made him well.

The soldier said to him, "Give me the drinking glass, and I will release you from your pledge."

The demon gave him the drinking glass, and the soldier thanked him and gave him his release, and the demon went away.

The soldier used the drinking glass whenever he was called upon to divine whether a person would live or die, and his fame spread throughout the land.

It happened one time that the Prince became ill, and he called the soldier to his side, saying, "Tell me what my destiny is." The soldier filled the glass with clear water and looked into it. And then he became sad, for he saw Death standing at the Prince's head and not at his feet. He said, "My friend and brother, no power on earth can save you, for Death stands at your head."

The Prince grew angry. He cried out, "You have saved generals and princes throughout the world, and now you will not save me who befriended you? If this is friendship, so be it." And he ordered that a scaffold be built and that the soldier be hanged.

The soldier thought about what the Prince had said. "If I have to die anyway, at least I may be able to save the

Prince," he thought. So he called on Death and said to him, "Let me change with the Prince. I will take his span of life and he may have mine." He looked again into the drinking glass, and this time he saw Death standing at the Prince's feet. He knew that Death had accepted his offer. He sprinkled the water from the glass on the Prince, and the Prince became well. Then he said to Death, "Give me three hours so that I may say good-by to my family." Death agreed, and the soldier went home.

When he arrived there, he was already feeling feeble, and he crawled into his bed, while Death stood at the head. "Say good-by, for the time is short," Death said.

But the soldier drew his magic knapsack from underneath his pillow and cried out, "Enter my knapsack, oh Death!" And Death entered the knapsack, because he couldn't help it, and the soldier closed it tightly and leaped from bed restored to health. He carried the knapsack to the center of the great forest, and tied it to the very top of a green aspen, left it there, and went away.

From that hour onward Death bothered no one, and life abounded all over the earth, and no one died.

The years came and passed. One day the soldier was riding along the road and he saw an old woman, withered and feeble, hardly able to walk. He greeted her and commented upon her great age. She looked at him with eyes full of weariness. She said: "Death should have come to me long ago. Years ago I had lived out my life and was just about ready to die, but someone captured Death and hid him away, and now I must live on and on, though I am tired and my body cries for peace. What is there for me to do?"

The soldier pondered over this, and at last he said, "I will set Death free, even though he takes me too."

He went into the forest and found the knapsack where he had hung it on the aspen tree. He called out, "Ho, Death, are you still there?" And Death replied, "I am here." The soldier took the knapsack back to his house. He opened it and Death came out. The soldier lay down on the bed to die. He said good-by to his wife and child and asked Death to take him then.

But Death replied, "You have offended me beyond forgiveness. I will not take you. Others I will take and relieve from suffering. As for you, may you live and suffer." And he went away to see those who needed him.

The soldier said, "If Death will not take me, I will go to the underworld by myself and ask them to take me." And he began his long journey. He traveled for many months and came at last to the frontiers of the underworld. There he was stopped by the demons who stood guard.

The gatekeepers cried out, "What do you want?"

"I want to enter and be thrown into the flames and be at peace."

"And what are you carrying on your back?"

"Only my knapsack."

And when the demons saw the knapsack they remembered the soldier and the way in which he had punished them. They beat an alarm, and guards came and bolted the gates.

The soldier called on Satan himself, the Prince of Darkness. "Take me in, I must rest at last."

Satan replied, "Return whence you came. You will never enter here."

"Then," the soldier said, "give me two hundred souls. I will take them and offer them to God, so that he may grant me relief for their sake."

"I will give you two hundred, and an extra fifty, if you go away at once and do not linger here."

The soldier took the souls released by Satan and carried them to Paradise. He knocked on the gate, and the keeper called out, "Who is there?"

"A soldier and two hundred and fifty souls, delivered from the flames of the underworld."

The message was taken to God, who said, "Admit the souls, but drive the soldier away."

And when the soldier heard God's decree he made a desperate plan. He gave his knapsack to one of the souls and instructed her, "When you are inside the gates, open the knapsack and cry, 'Enter my knapsack, soldier!' This way I can enter, there is no other way."

The gates were opened and the two hundred and fifty souls went in. And the one with the knapsack entered last. But when she found herself in Paradise, all things were forgotten from her mind, even the soldier who stood waiting outside the gates.

And thus the soldier was shut out, and he was forced to go back to the earth and live on and on.

THE SNAKE AND THE DREAMS
[*Union of Soviet Socialist Republics*]

In a certain land there was once a King who had a strange dream. As he slept he saw a fox hanging by the tail from the roof of the palace. When he awoke he remembered the dream and couldn't get it out of his mind. At last he called his ministers and counselors before him, asking if they could interpret the meaning of the fox hanging from the roof.

His advisers couldn't help him. And as his recollection of the dream continued to trouble him, he at last commanded that there be a great convocation in the city, and that everyone in the kingdom should attend. His hope was that among all the citizens of the country there would be someone wise enough to give him the answer.

The people began to assemble. One of those who came was a poor farmer named Ivan. On the way to the city he came to a rocky place where the trail was narrow. Lying in the center of the trail he saw a snake.

Ivan paused, and as he did so the snake spoke to him, saying, "Good day. Where are you going?"

Ivan told him about the King's command.

"But what is the use of it all?" Ivan asked. "How can I tell the King what his dream means?"

"There will be a reward for the man who gives the King

the right answer," the snake said. "Promise you will share the reward with me, and I will tell you what to say."

Ivan was glad. He said, "Certainly I will share with you if you tell me the correct answer. Half will be yours and half will be mine, and in addition I will be everlastingly grateful."

"Then here is the answer," the snake said. "The dream of the fox hanging from the palace roof means that there is cunning, deceit, and treachery in the kingdom."

The farmer thanked him and went on to the city. When his turn came, Ivan was brought before the King, and he interpreted the dream as the snake had advised him. So pleased was the King with the answer that he gave Ivan money and valuable presents. But when Ivan was ready to leave, he said to himself, "Why should I share these riches with a snake?" And he returned to his village by a different road, avoiding the place where the snake lived.

Later, the King had another dream that troubled him. In this dream he saw a sword hanging from the roof. He sent for Ivan immediately, because Ivan had given so wise an explanation of the first dream. Ivan was now afraid, for he knew he had no special talents for explaining dreams. There was no choice but to look for the snake. He went to the narrow trail, but he saw no snake there. He called for him, saying, "Snake, come for a moment, I must talk to you!" He kept calling this way until at last the snake came out of his hole.

"What troubles you, and what do you want of me?" the snake asked him.

"The King has had another dream," Ivan said. "What shall I tell him?"

"I will give you the answer if you share the reward with me," the snake said.

"I will share, I promise," Ivan replied.

"Tell the King that the sword hanging from the roof is a sign of coming war," the snake said. "Enemies are plotting against him within the kingdom as well as outside the kingdom. Bloodshed is at hand. The King must prepare to defend the country."

Ivan thanked the snake and went on to the city. When the King asked him for an interpretation of the dream, he repeated what the snake had said. Again the King was deeply impressed with what he heard, and he gave Ivan many valuable presents.

But Ivan became angry at the thought of having to share with a snake. He came to the place where the snake was waiting. The snake said, "Now give me the half which is mine."

"I'll give you nothing but trouble!" Ivan shouted. He drew his knife and attacked the snake, which turned and fled into its hole. But just as it was disappearing, Ivan brought his knife down and cut off the snake's tail. Then he went on home, thinking no more of the matter and rejoicing in his new wealth.

Time passed. A bloody war came, as predicted, but the King's armies were victorious. Then the King had another dream. This time he saw a sheep hanging from the roof. Again Ivan was sent for. And this time he was worried and afraid. "For," he said, "how can I go now to the snake for help? I have deceived it and wounded it with my weapon."

But he had no choice. So he went by the same path, and when he came to the rocky place he called the snake until at last it came. Ivan told of his problem, and the snake answered, as before, "If you promise to give me half of your reward, I will give you the answer."

"I will do it," Ivan said.

"Then here is the answer to the King's dream," the snake said. "The sheep hanging from the roof means that everywhere now there is peace in the land, and that people are contented."

Ivan went to the palace and gave the King the answer. So pleased was the King with what he heard that he gave Ivan more presents and money than ever before.

This time Ivan came back by the same route, and he found the snake waiting. He gave half of his presents to the snake, saying, "You have been patient with me, even though I have abused you. Here is half of what I received this time, and when I return home I will send you half of what I received before. Forgive me for the way I mistreated you."

The snake listened, and he replied, "Do not feel too badly about what has happened. It was not your fault. The first time, if you remember the King's dream of the fox, the land was full of deceit, hypocrisy, and treachery. You too were a deceiver, for you went home by another road so as to avoid me. But you were simply one among many, and deceit was in the air.

"The second time, if you remember, was a time of war, quarrels, and assassination. Cruelty was everywhere. You were only one of many, and your brutality in cutting off my tail was a brutality shared by everyone.

"But now that peace hangs over us all, like everyone else you are generous and just, and you share your gifts with me.   Go, brother, and may the peace of God remain with you.   I have no need of your wealth."

And the snake went away and disappeared into its hole.

THE CONTRARY WIFE
[*Norway*]

There was once a villager who had the bad luck to have a contrary wife. So perverse was she that other contrary people seem well-mannered and considerate by comparison. It was bad enough for her neighbors. If someone said the parson had given a good sermon, she would say it was a bad one. If the fishseller had only herring to sell, she would demand smelt. If he offered her fresh fish, she wanted it salted; if he had salted, she wanted fresh. When someone noticed the wind blowing from the east, she found that it was coming from the north.

But if it was bad for the neighbors, it was endlessly miserable for her husband. When he thought it would be nice to visit his brother on a Sunday, she would correct him, saying that it would be better to visit her sister. When he would ask her to mend a shirt, she would say no, it was his sock that needed darning. If he wanted beer, he would get tea. If he asked for tea, he would get water. Sometimes the neighbors complained to him about his wife. He would say: "Good neighbor, why do *you* complain? When you go into your house at night you hear no more of my wife. As for me, I live with her. There's no end to my misery. When I eat fast, she says to go slowly. If I sleep on my back, she wakes me to tell me to turn over."

One morning the villager and his contrary wife went out

to inspect their rye field. They crossed the river and looked at the grain closely.

"The rye will be ready for harvest on Tuesday," the man said.

"Monday," his wife corrected him.

"Very well, Monday," the man said. "I'll get Halvard and Hans to help."

"You'll do nothing of the sort," his wife corrected him. "You'll get Thore and Erik to help."

The poor villager was so used to this sort of thing he said, "Yes, of course, Thore and Erik." And thinking aloud, rather than speaking to his wife, he said, "We'll start at seven in the morning."

But his wife said, "Six-thirty."

"The weather's likely to be good this week," he said, looking at the sky.

"No, it will surely rain," his wife said, also looking at the sky.

The villager was getting fed up, but he'd had so much practice at this sort of thing that he held his temper.

"Rain or shine, we'll reap with scythes."

"Scythes, did you say?" his wife asked, her voice rising. "You'll cut with shears."

"Cut with shears?" the man asked, stopping in his tracks. "Whoever heard of harvesting a field with shears? We'll reap with scythes."

"Shears," the woman said firmly.

As they argued, they crossed the bridge.

"Scythes!" the man said angrily.

"Shears!" the wife replied. "Shears!"

So angry was she at being argued with that she didn't look where she was going, and she fell off the bridge into the water. It was deep where she fell in, and she disappeared from sight. But when she bobbed to the surface she shouted—not "Help!" or "Save me!" but "Shears!" She sank again, and when she rose to the top the man just had time to call back, "Scythes!" before she disappeared. In a moment she was back, coughing and sputtering and shouting, "Shears! Shears!" She sank again, and when her head reappeared in the swirling water her husband spoke in a determined and calm voice, "It will be scythes!" The obstinate woman came to the surface once more, but she was too weak to talk. She went down slowly, without uttering a word, but as her head went under her hand came out of the water, and with her fingers she made the motions of a shears opening and closing. Then she was seen no more.

The villager went back to get his friends, Thore and Erik, Halvard and Hans. They all searched together for the woman, but they could find no trace of her near the bridge.

"Let us look downstream," one of them said. "Surely the water has carried her away."

So they went downstream and looked, but there was no sign of her.

"Where could she have gone?" the men asked each other.

Suddenly the villager slapped his head.

"How could I have lived so long with this woman without guessing what she would do at a time like this!" he exclaimed. "There is no one in God's world like her. Other people would float downstream, that is true. But not she.

161

She is too contrary.   Would she go along reasonably with the current?   No, not that woman!   We'd better look upstream by the dam."

So they went upstream past the bridge, and as the villager had guessed, they found her there, trying to float upwards over the dam itself.

SALT AND BREAD
[*Sweden*]

There was once a King with three daughters. The two older girls were jealous of the youngest, whom the King loved dearly, and they spent much time and effort trying to destroy the King's love for her. They tried to win special favors and privileges from their father, never missing an opportunity to suggest that the youngest girl did not return his affection. Their evil jealousy wouldn't let them rest. At last the King became troubled over the rumors he heard from the older daughters. He even became suspicious of the youngest girl. And one day when the three daughters were with him, he could not refrain from putting their love to a test.

So he asked the oldest girl to tell him how much she loved him, and she replied:

"I value you, my father, as God in Heaven!"

Her answer pleased the King. He then asked the second daughter the same question, and she replied:

"Oh my father, I value you as my own life!"

This answer also pleased the King. And he turned now to the youngest daughter, asking her how she would describe her feelings. She answered:

"Oh my father, I value you as salt and bread."

The King was startled by this reply. Then he became angry that she cared no more for him than the humblest things on a poor man's table. His anger turned to fury that his youngest daughter, on whom he had lavished so much affection, thought so little of him in return. And he ordered his servants to drive her out of his house. They did as they were told, and took her into the woods and abandoned her. Now, at last, the two older daughters were happy.

In the woods, the youngest daughter was miserable and frightened. She cried when she thought about the home and the father she loved. She could not understand his anger, nor why she had been banished. She wandered about the woods helplessly, and at last, in fear of the wild animals, she climbed into a tall tree.

It happened that a King from another country at that moment was hunting in the woods. As he rode along on his horse, he heard his dogs barking with excitement. He hurried after them and found them surrounding the tree where the Princess was hiding. He looked upward, expecting to find a bear. Instead, he saw the beautiful face of the unhappy girl. He spoke to her kindly and asked her to come down.

He put the girl on his horse and took her to his castle. There he fed her and warmed her before a log fire. At last, overcome by his kindness, the Princess poured out her story. The King was impressed with her goodness as well as her beauty. He cared for her in his castle, and at last he asked her to marry him. The girl, too, had fallen in love, and she agreed.

So a date was set for the wedding, and invitations were sent to the royalty of the seven neighboring kingdoms.

When the wedding day came, the royal guests arrived. Among them were the young Princess's father and her two older sisters. They did not recognize her, so sure were they that the Princess had disappeared forever in the woods.

When they took their seats at the banquet table, wonderful food of all kinds was set before the guests. But none of the food was salted, and there was no salt on the table. Neither was there bread.

At last the girl's father could not refrain from commenting, and he said, "I don't understand, but it seems to me that two most precious things are missing from this feast."

"Ah?" the Princess, now a Queen, replied. "What can you be speaking of?"

"Why," her father replied, "salt and bread."

"Yes," the girl said. "They are among the most precious things we know. And once because I valued my father as highly as these things I was driven out of his house and into the woods to die."

When her father heard these words he was overcome. He recognized her and embraced her with a cry of joy, thankful and happy that she was alive and well. He begged her forgiveness for his misunderstanding of her words of affection and for his having driven her away.

As for the older sisters, their plot against the youngest was now exposed, and it was their turn to be turned out of their father's house. From that day on, no more was ever heard of them. If they were ever rescued from the woods by hunting kings, nobody has ever heard about it.

THE TALISMAN
[Denmark]

A Prince and a Princess were still celebrating their honeymoon. They were extremely happy; only one thought disturbed them, and that was how to retain their present happiness. For that reason they wished to own a talisman with which to protect them against any unhappiness in their marriage.

Now, they had often been told about a man who lived out in the forest, acclaimed by everybody for his wisdom and known for his good advice in every need and difficulty. So the Prince and Princess called upon him and told him about their heart's desire. After the wise man had listened to them he said, "Travel through every country in the world, and wherever you meet a completely happily married couple, ask them for a small piece of the linen they wear close to the body, and when you receive this, you must always carry it on you. That is a sure remedy!"

The Prince and Princess rode forth, and on their way they soon heard of a knight and his wife who were said to be living the most happily married life. They went to the knight's castle and asked him and his wife if their marriage was truly as happy as was rumored.

"Yes, of course," was the answer, "with the one exception that we have no children."

Here, then, the talisman was not to be found, and the

Prince and Princess continued their journey in search of the completely happily married couple.

As they traveled on, they came to a country where they heard of an honest citizen who lived in perfect unity and happiness with his wife. So to him they went, and asked if he was really as happily married as people said.

"Yes, I am," the man answered. "My wife and I live in perfect harmony; if only we didn't have so many children, for they give us a lot of worries and sorrows!"

So neither with him was the talisman to be found, and the Prince and Princess continued their journey through the country, always inquiring about happily married couples but none presented themselves.

One day, as they rode along fields and meadows, they noticed a shepherd close by the road, cheerfully playing his flute. Just then a woman carrying a child in her arm, and holding a little boy by the hand, walked towards him. As soon as the shepherd saw her, he greeted her and took the little child, whom he kissed and caressed. The shepherd's dog ran to the boy, licked his little hand, and barked and jumped with joy. In the meantime the woman arranged a meal she had brought along, and then said, "Father, come and eat now!" The man sat down and took of the food, but the first bite he gave to the little boy, and the second he divided between the boy and the dog. All this was observed by the Prince and Princess, who walked closer, and spoke to them, saying, "You must be a truly happily married couple."

"Yes, that we are," said the man. "God be praised; no prince or princess could be happier than we are!"

"Now listen then," said the Prince. "Do us a favor, and you shall never regret it. Give us a small piece of the linen garment you wear close to your body!"

As he spoke, the shepherd and his wife looked strangely at each other, and finally he said, "God knows, we would be only too happy to give you not only a small piece, but the whole shirt, or undergarment, if we only had them, but we own not as much as a rag!"

So the Prince and Princess journeyed on, their mission unaccomplished. Finally, their unsuccessful roaming discouraged them, and they decided to return home. As they passed the wise man's hut, they stopped by, related all their travel experiences, and reproached him for giving them such poor advice.

At that the wise man smiled and said, "Has your trip really been in vain? Are you not returning richer in knowledge?"

"Yes," answered the Prince, "I have gained *this* knowledge, that contentment is a rare gift on this earth."

"And I have learned," said the Princess, "that to be contented one needs nothing more than simply—to be contented!"

Whereupon the Prince took the Princess's hand; they looked at each other with an expression of deepest love. And the wise man blessed them and said, "In your own hearts you have found the true talisman! Guard it carefully, and the evil spirit of discontentment shall never in all eternity have any power over you!"

THE FIDDLER OF ECHTERNACH

[*Luxembourg*]

Once, long ago, it is said, there lived in the town of Echternach a citizen by the name of Veit. This man went with his wife on a pilgrimage to the Holy Land. During the long journey his wife died, and when Veit returned sorrowing to his own country he was alone. It is told that his wife's relatives had disapproved of the marriage in the first place, and when Veit came home without his wife they saw their chance to bring bad fortune upon him and to seize all his land and money. And so they accused him of having murdered his wife and had him arrested. During his trial, his wife's relatives gave false testimony, and Veit was condemned to death.

There was a great stir in the town on the day fixed for his execution. As a huge crowd gathered around the scaffold, ready to revel in the plight of the helpless man, Veit walked calmly to the place where he was to be hanged. There was a faraway look in his eyes as he stood between the executioners. He paid no attention to the shouts of the mob. His only companion was his violin, which he held in his arms.

Standing on the scaffold, he looked at the crowd. The jeering and abuse rose to a roar. In all those faces in front of him, Veit could see no pity, nor did he hear a voice raised to pray for his soul. In the very front of this dreadful gathering, Veit could see his wife's relations, their faces reflecting vindictive triumph and insatiable greed. Their cries were the loudest and their abuse the vilest of all. They alone knew he was innocent, yet they were the ones who had brought him to the scaffold.

At last, slowly and with dignity, Veit raised his hand for silence. The jeers died down, the people nudged each other and cupped their hands over their ears to hear better. The condemned man was about to make his last request. His voice was calm as he spoke.

"Citizens, I have a last request to make! Let me play one more tune on my beloved violin."

His words were followed by hoots and catcalls, but Veit tucked his violin under his chin and began to play. Hardly were the first notes heard before a great silence fell upon the crowd. Clear and sweet, the music rose upon the morning air. It floated into the hills beyond the town and rose to meet the fleecy clouds above them. It lingered over the river and swept down the valley. Sweet, plaintive, appealing, irresistible, it seemed to plead to the heavens themselves for mercy and justice.

The executioners were the first to begin to dance. Slowly at first, shuffling and reluctant, their feet began to move in time to the music. Then the mayor, the priest, and the chief officer followed their example. Their faces showed bewilderment, wonder, and fear.

Soon the crowd began to join in the dance: young folk, old folk, widows, and grandmothers, old men and children, policemen and soldiers, rich and poor. They became frenzied and helpless in their ecstasy. They stamped their feet, flung out their arms, and whirled around in a fury of rhythm. Soon, the people from the houses, from the nearby villages, from the valley, and from the hills came pouring into the town to join the dance.

Then began to come cries of "Have pity, have mercy, stop playing or we die!" The people who had testified falsely against Veit in the trial began to cry, "We wronged you, we told wicked lies, you are innocent! Only stop playing and you shall go free!"

Their shouting rose to a frenzied scream, but the grim, solitary figure of the violinist continued to play more and more passionately.

The day wore on. The older people looked ready to die from fatigue, the children were crying, and thousands of hands were raised in supplication to the merciless man on the scaffold.

At last evening came. As the sky turned red with the setting sun, the fiddler descended slowly from the scaffold. When he passed through the maddened, helpless throng, their ranks gave way before him, and no one could touch him or his magic violin. Thus, still playing, he passed through the town and out into the hills beyond. Soon he vanished from sight, never to be seen again.

But the magic tune still filled the air, and still the people danced. That night the priest Willibrord came to the town, and, when he saw the plight of those thousands of people who could not stop their frenzied dancing, he fell on his knees and prayed to God to have mercy on them.

Nobody had thought of doing this for poor Veit that morning, and nobody deserved the deliverance for which the good Willibrord prayed. Nevertheless, the music slowly died away, and one by one the people dropped exhausted. Only for the relatives who had conspired against Veit was there no relief, for they danced on and on until they died in their tracks. For the rest of the people there was nothing to do but to crawl home in agony and sleep, sleep, sleep. But no one forgot the lesson that was learned that day.

And each year since that time, on the Tuesday of Pentacost week, there has been a great procession in Echternach. The crowd moves through the town doing a curious jumping dance which ends at the steps of the old cathedral. Old people say the event is in memory of the evil day when Veit was led to the gallows.

THE BRIDGE OF ST. CLOUD
[*France*]

The people of St. Cloud had long needed a bridge across the River Seine, and at last after many debates and arguments the money was raised, the plans were approved, craftsmen were engaged, and work was started.   But in all the bustle of preparation, someone must have forgotten to ask for the appropriate blessings on the undertaking, for it seemed as though an evil spell lay over the work and the builders could not make any progress.   Scaffolds collapsed into the river, stones were mysteriously displaced or broken in the night, and all kinds of mishaps occurred, so that the workmen were almost afraid even to pick up their tools. The master mason who was in charge was baffled; all his efforts to find out who or what was responsible for the trouble were unavailing and he didn't know what to do. One day he lost patience completely.   Throwing down the roll of plans which he carried in his hands and mopping the sweat from his brow, he cried angrily, "I've had enough of this!   No one but the devil could finish this job, and he can, for all I care!"

And he stamped furiously away.

The Bailiff of St. Cloud, who had just reached the spot on a visit of inspection, was as baffled as the master mason; it seemed that nothing had been accomplished since his last visit a week before, yet the men had been toiling as hard

as ever.   Sighing heavily, he turned and made his way homeward, sunk in thought.   So preoccupied was he with all his
troubles that he didn't notice a tall, dark stranger who stood
in his path until the stranger spoke to him.

"Master Bailiff," said the stranger, "may I have a word
with you?"

Startled out of his gloomy reflections, the Bailiff snapped,
"That depends on what it's about."

The stranger smiled.   "It's about your bridge," he said.

"Ah," replied the Bailiff, "speak, then.   But I'm afraid,
after what I have just seen, that you won't be able to say
anything good about it."

"Your bridge isn't coming along very well, is it?" the
stranger said.

"You know it isn't," the Bailiff answered.

"Small wonder," the stranger said.   "You know, it never
will be finished unless I take a hand."

The Bailiff brightened.

"Are you a mason, then?" he asked.

The stranger laughed.

"No, my dear Bailiff.   A mason couldn't help you.   I
am the Devil.   And believe me, when I put my mind to it
I can build both well and swiftly."

The Bailiff was even more startled than before, but he
managed to control himself.

"Master Devil," he said, "you've come at the right time,
I must say.   But we can't discuss this matter here, in the
middle of the street; it might cause gossip.   Here is my
house.   Come inside so that we can talk quietly."

174

They went into the house. The Bailiff turned to his wife and said, "I have business to do; close the shutters, keep the servants quiet, and see that no one disturbs us."

The Bailiff's wife went away to do as she had been told, and the Bailiff addressed his visitor.

"Let's put our cards on the table. We need the bridge desperately; the people cannot carry on their trade without it—in fact, it's almost a matter of life or death for the town. And yet, for all our efforts, the confounded thing has brought us nothing but trouble."

"You surprise me!" the Devil replied, grinning.

"Anyway, we are ready, Master Devil, to pay any price—even to submit to new taxes—to get the bridge finished. You say you can help—how much do you want? How many gold pieces will it cost to finish the bridge?"

"Now, Master Bailiff," the Devil said, grinning again, "what would I do with your gold? I have as much of it as I want, whenever I want it. See!"

The Devil reached into the fireplace and with his bare hand took out a glowing ember. He blew on it and held it out to the Bailiff.

"Stop, don't do that!" the Bailiff cried, drawing back.

"Can't you trust me?" asked the Devil, as he placed in the Bailiff's hand a bar of the purest gold, glittering but quite cold. The Bailiff fingered it gingerly, and gave it back.

"Keep it, my dear friend, keep it," said the Devil, airily waving his hand. "That's nothing to me; the merest trifle. It shall serve, if you like, to seal our bargain."

"We've made no bargain yet," said the Bailiff, pocketing

the gold nevertheless, "but I can well understand that if gold costs you so little effort you will want to be paid in some other currency."

"Well yes, but between ourselves, not so much; I'll finish the bridge for you if you will promise me the soul of the first living creature to cross it when I have done."

"Well now," mused the Bailiff, "I don't know whether I have the right. . . ."

"Of course you have!" cried the Devil. "I know what I am talking about in these matters. I assure you it's the usual thing." The Devil rose to his feet and made as if to leave. "Is it yes or no?"

"You want the first living creature who crosses the bridge? But what will you do with him?"

"That's my business," said the Devil, "but use your imagination; what do you think I'll do? Come now, draw up the agreement—you have paper, ink, and a pen on your desk there. . . ."

The Bailiff sat down at his desk, took up a pen, and drew a sheet of paper towards him, and inquired, "What shall I write?"

The Devil dictated, and the Bailiff wrote out the contract, according to which the Devil agreed to finish the bridge in six days, in return for the soul of the first living creature who would cross it on the seventh. Each signed the paper, and the Devil went to work.

Soon, to the astonishment and joy of the people of St. Cloud, a beautiful new bridge spanned the river. But the Bailiff had told the story of the pact he had made with the Devil and had warned everybody of the fate awaiting the first to cross the bridge, and all of them were afraid to approach.

And so, on the seventh day, the crowd which had come to admire the new structure watched from afar to see what would happen. In a little while the spectators gasped with astonishment—the Bailiff himself was seen, walking with determined steps along the road leading to the bridge.

"Well now!" said the Devil, who, seated on the parapet, was awaiting his wages. "That's what I call real devotion to the public service! I know that hell is already full of bailiffs, but, never mind, one can never have too many."

Licking his lips, the Devil stretched out his claws towards the Bailiff, but the latter, paying no attention whatever to the devil's mockery, stopped at the very instant when he was about to set foot on the bridge and, holding out his arm, shook his wide sleeve. A cat which he had concealed there leapt out and, wild with fright, sped like an arrow in front of the Devil and over the bridge.

"There is your payment, Master Devil!" cried the Bailiff. "That is the first living thing to cross the bridge! And if you want to collect your wages you'd better run after it!"

Thereupon all the church bells of St. Cloud began to ring a triumphant peal; the bishops and the clergy formed into a procession and, with banners flying, marched across the bridge, dedicating to God the work of the Devil, while the latter, raging but powerless, fled.

THE LADY OF STAVOREN

[*The Netherlands*]

In days long ago, before the fair green meadows of Friesland had been united with Holland, Stavoren was one of the mightiest cities in that province. Its towers and spires rose about the Zuyder Zee in majestic splendor. Ah, there was a city for you—a city of stately palaces and splendid public buildings, of rich burghers and strutting nobles.

The reason for all this prosperity was that Stavoren had a beautiful harbor, one of the finest in Friesland. Its ships, without number, spread their proud sails to the wind and rode all the seven seas. As time passed, Stavoren became so rich that its burghers began to put golden handles on their doors and golden hinges on their windows. They went even further: in front of their houses they built stoops of pure gold, fenced in with golden railings. Then they began to throw out their chests and to step very high, and they tilted their noses in the air and pointed across the Zuyder Zee to where the lantern in the white cupola of the great Drommedaris Tower kept guard over the fortifications and harbor of Enkhuisen, in Holland.

"Over there in Holland," the burghers would say, "they have no such city as Stavoren. Enkhuisen has no citizens who can afford to build stoops of solid gold." And, having said that, they strutted more proudly than ever before.

Now of all the vain and haughty people in Stavoren none

was vainer or more haughty than a certain rich widow.   Her
husband had been a shipowner, and he had left her a treasure
so immense that none knew its real extent.   She would pass
through the streets with jewels glittering on her long, white
fingers and all over her splendid robes, and she held her head
so high that she scarcely even saw the poorer folk, who
bobbed little curtsies as she passed and paid humble respect
to such a mighty display.   There were few in the city who
did not stand in awe of her.

"Ah," they would say, "she is the richest woman in Stavoren!"   And alas, poor souls, they knew of nothing better
than that to say about any living being.   They held nothing else to be of value but riches, riches, riches.   Many envied the rich widow, many feared her, and a few strove to
outshine her.

One day a certain ship belonging to her was about to set
sail with a rich cargo to trade in far ports of the world.

"Ha," said the widow to herself, "it's time I acquired
something to startle those boorish burghers who think themselves so grand.   It's time I made them see that their riches
are but a pinch of sand compared to treasures such as mine!"

And she sent at once for the skipper who commanded the
vessel.   When the honest old fellow stood respectfully before her, she said: "I order you to search the world and to
bring back to me in your ship the richest, most beautiful,
and most precious thing to be bought for gold.

"Spare no money or pains," she commanded.   "I have
ordered your vessel to be laden with gold coins.   Exchange
them for the most precious thing in the world."

The old skipper stood for a moment perplexed.   How

179

should he know what was the most beautiful and precious thing in the world? But he was a sturdy fellow with a just respect for his own intelligence, so he answered, "I shall obey you, my lady. I shall bring you back the richest, most beautiful, and most precious thing in the world."

The very next day his ship set sail. For many a day thereafter the skipper pondered over the task his mistress had set him. In the rich and magnificent cities of the East, he saw scores of costly and splendid things—the noble work of goldsmiths, bracelets, rings, sparkling diamonds, embroidered cloths, Byzantine tapestry, gold brocade—but he was a simple man of the people, and their glitter had no charm for him and cast no spell over him whatever. He had not been born in Stavoren. As a boy he had lived among the rich, green meadows of Friesland, with not a single golden stoop in sight. How should such a man value ivory, or diamonds, or gold brocade? To him they were nothing but vain things —toys that were neither precious nor beautiful.

No, in those magnificent Eastern cities he could not find the most beautiful and precious thing in the world. Indeed, he had almost given up hope of ever finding it, when he chanced to sail into the harbor of Danzig. As he was roaming about the streets of the city he passed a plain-looking building, and inside it he saw something that set his heart leaping for joy, a beautiful hoard of golden treasure—bushels and bushels of golden wheat.

In all the world what was more beautiful and precious than wheat? Wheat, whence came bread, the very staff of life, the gift whereby men renewed their strength for the joyous work of the day. Ivory and peacocks and diamonds might vanish from the earth and men be none the worse, but wheat they must have for their comfort and happiness. The skipper's face glowed.

"Where have my wits been all these months?" he asked himself. "Any simple Frisian knows there is nothing in the world more beautiful or more precious than wheat. At last I have found what my mistress desires. I shall take it home to her."

And he loaded his vessel forthwith and set sail again for Stavoren.

Meanwhile the rich widow had been for months impatiently awaiting his return. Day in and day out, she kept fancying what all the people in Stavoren would say when they saw the wondrous treasure her ship was to bring her.

"And that fellow, Halbertsma, will stop trying to outshine me when he sees what I shall have then," she said to herself. "And Mevrouw Cirksena will eat humble pie when she looks at me in my splendor!" She even boasted far and near of what her ship would bring home.

At length the great day came. Children, running through the streets, shouted in great excitement that the ship was in the harbor. The widow decked herself out in her costliest garments, and off she went to the dock, scarcely able to wait till the ship was made fast to the shore. No one indeed stayed at home that day. All Stavoren hurried off to the wharf—men, women, and children, eagerly flocking to catch a glimpse of the widow's much-vaunted treasure.

"It will be diamonds as big as eggs," some people cried.

"It will be rubies the size of bricks, and turquoises as big as your head," cried others.

The Captain sprang ashore, his honest fact glowing with joy.

"Well," said the lady, her voice trembling with expectancy. "What have you brought me?"

"The finest treasure in all the world."

"Yes, but what is it, what is it?"

"Wheat," answered the Captain with quiet satisfaction. "A shipload of wheat!"

"Wheat!" stammered the widow, painfully astonished. "You have brought me wheat?"

"Wheat!" cried the crowd and they all began to snicker. "Wheat! Her wonderful treasure is nothing but common, everyday wheat." Their snicker became a jeer. The rich woman who had lorded it over them so often and boasted so haughtily—she had nothing to show them but wheat, common everyday wheat! Did you ever hear the like?

What a day for my lady, the widow! All those gibes and jeers from the very men, women, and children she had thought to overawe were like so many barbs in her flesh. And what hurts a vain woman more than mockery? When she could control her voice enough to speak, she cried in rage, "So! In return for my rich cargo you have brought me back wheat?"

"Yes, Mevrouw!"

"Well, you can take the wretched stuff out to the entrance of the harbor and dump it into the sea!"

The Captain was struck dumb. She did not like his

182

precious wheat, his beautiful, useful, golden wheat. He could not understand. To him it was a sacred thing.

"No, no!" he cried in great distress. "Don't dump it in the sea!" To throw away food, yes, even a crust or a few crumbs of bread, was that not a monstrous sin? Wheat was God's precious gift to man, and man must treat it with reverence and gratitude. "If you do not care to keep it," he urged, "I pray you, give it to the poor. Many could be fed with that cargo. To throw it into the sea would be so great a sin that it might bring punishment on your head and reduce you to poverty, yes, even to dire distress!"

At this the widow grew white with anger. Taking a beautiful ring from her finger, she threw it scornfully into the water and cried, "Do as you are bid. I fear neither punishment nor distress. As surely as I shall never see that ring again, so surely can I never be poor and in want. Dump the wheat in the sea!"

Slowly and sadly, the good Captain turned the vessel about and returned to the entrance of the harbor. Not a voice on shore called him back. Not a voice among all those burghers of Stavoren was raised in protest to save the wheat. One and all, they despised it. They had no respect save for things that glittered. They knew not the value and beauty of simple, homely wheat. They loved only idle show. Had they not built stoops of pure gold with no other purpose than just to show off, to make all the world understand how much greater they were than the good folk of Enkhuisen in Holland across the Zuyder Zee?

It was a sad moment for the Captain—dumping his wheat in the sea. No more would he serve the Lady of Stavoren.

There was an end of that! He must seek a master who understood the real value of things.

And what of the haughty widow? In deepest chagrin, she went back to her home, and scarce did she dare to show her nose out of doors again, for, whenever she poked but the tip of it forth, some monkey-faced imp of a boy would gibe, "Say, lady when is your next treasure ship coming home?"

Worse than that, no more than two days later it chanced that she ordered fish to be served for her dinner. Suddenly, one of her servants came running into her presence, painfully excited, and bearing a fish in his hand. What had he found in its stomach? Her ring! The ring that she had cast into the sea! She grew pale, for well she remembered her words: "As surely as I shall never see this ring again, so surely can I never be poor and in want! Dump the wheat in the sea!" And there was her ring come back!

In that selfsame hour the widow received news that one of her ships had been lost in a storm, and during the months that followed many such tidings reached her.

And those haughty burghers of Stavoren who thought they should never want . . . !

The very next spring, above the waves of the sea at the entrance to the city's splendid harbor, an ominous green appeared. The wheat, which the burghers had so despised, had taken root and sprung up, only now it grew as a weed and bore no precious fruit, not a single golden grain.

As the days went by, the floating currents of sand which continually sweep around the Zuyder Zee began to catch in the stalks of wheat and to stick there, until they had piled up a sandbank—a huge, immovable wall of sand, that closed in Stavoren's harbor. No more could the great ships, which had once glided so easily into port, enter the bay at Stavoren. They could not pass the bar. Stavoren was shut in forever.

And so the city lost its harbor, the very source of its wealth. The proud lady's ships could no longer sail the seven seas. Slowly her treasures melted away; her gold, her jewels, her palaces, and the wealth of her neighbors likewise vanished into nothing. There were no more golden stoops. Stavoren dwindled and dwindled. With each succeeding year it grew smaller and less important, until by and by the world forgot it, shut in behind its sandbank.

And so it came about that where once a haughty city stood there is now but a sleepy village—a few little, gabled, red-roofed houses, half hidden in broad old trees. But everyone remembers still the story of the proud widow; and the sand bank, which spoiled the harbor, is called to this very day, "Vrouwenzand," or "Lady's Sand."

THE SOUP STONE
[*Belgium*]

One day a soldier was walking home from the wars and came to a village. The wind was cold; the sky was gray; and the soldier was hungry. He stopped at a house on the edge of the village and asked for something to eat. "We have nothing for ourselves," the people said, so the soldier went on.

He stopped at the next house and asked for something to eat. "We have nothing ourselves," the people said.

"Have you got a big pot?" the soldier said. Yes, they had a big iron pot.

"Have you got water?" he asked. Yes, they had plenty of water.

"Fill the pot with water and put it on the fire," the soldier said, "for I have a soup stone with me."

"A soup stone?" they said. "What is that?"

"It is a stone that makes soup," the soldier replied. And they all gathered round to see this wonder.

The woman of the house filled the big pot with water and hung it over the fire. The soldier took a stone from his pocket (it looked like any stone a man might pick up on the road) and tossed it into the pot. "Now let it boil," he said. So they all sat down to wait for the pot to boil.

"Could you spare a bit of salt for it?" the soldier asked.

"Of course," the woman said, and she pulled out the salt

box. The soldier took a fistful of salt and threw it in, for it was a big pot. Then they all sat back to wait.

"A few carrots would taste good in it," the soldier said longingly.

"Oh, we have a few carrots," the woman said, and she pulled them out from under a bench, where the soldier had been eying them. So they threw in the carrots. And while the carrots boiled, the soldier told them stories of his adventures.

"A few potatoes would be good, wouldn't they?" the soldier said. "They'd thicken the soup a bit."

"We have a few potatoes," said the oldest girl. "I'll get them." So they put the potatoes in the pot and waited for the soup to boil.

"An onion does give a good flavor," the soldier said.

"Run next door and ask the neighbor for an onion," the farmer told his smallest son. The child ran out of the house and came back with three onions. So they put the onions in. While they were waiting, they were cracking jokes and telling tales.

". . . And I haven't tasted cabbage since I left my mother's house," the soldier was saying.

"Run out in the garden and pull a cabbage," said the mother. And a small girl ran out and came back with a cabbage. And they put that in.

"It won't be long now," the soldier said.

"Just a little longer," the woman said, stirring the pot with a long ladle.

At that moment the oldest son came in. He had been hunting and brought home two rabbits.

"Just what we need for the finishing touch!" cried the soldier, and it was only a matter of minutes before the rabbits were cut up and thrown into the pot.

"Ha!" said the hungry hunter. "The smell of a fine soup."

"The traveler has brought a soup stone," the farmer said to his son, "and he is making soup with it in the pot."

At last the soup was ready, and it was good. There was enough for all: the soldier and the farmer and his wife, the oldest girl and the oldest son, the little girl, and the little son.

"It's a wonderful soup," the farmer said.

"It's a wonderful stone," the wife said.

"It is," the soldier said, "and it will make soup forever if you follow the formula we used today."

So they finished the soup. And when the soldier said good-by, he gave the woman the stone to pay back the kindness. She protested politely.

"It's nothing," the soldier said and went on his way without the stone.

Luckily, he found another just before he came to the next village.

KING JOHN AND
THE ABBOT OF CANTERBURY
[Great Britain]

King John of England was a cruel and jealous man. He couldn't bear the thought that anyone else in the kingdom might have wealth or popularity. If anyone at all was to have power and be envied, it was to be King John himself. He wielded his authority recklessly, and he was ruthless toward those whom he believed threatened his absolute control of the country.

It is said that King John heard one day that the Abbot of Canterbury had amassed great wealth. It was whispered that the Abbot kept a magnificent house, with costly furnishings and a hundred men to guard and wait upon him. It was rumored that the Abbot's servants even wore golden chains around their necks. When King John heard these things he became angry, for such a life, he thought, was fit only for the King. So he sent for the Abbot and said to him sternly, "How now, Father Abbot! It is said that your house is bigger and richer than the King's. Do you think this is seemly and proper?"

"My Liege Lord," the Abbot replied humbly, "this tale is false. I am not a rich man, and everyone knows that I never spend a penny that is not mine."

"Do you mean perhaps that I do?" King John said in anger. "You should die for this grievous insult!"

"I meant no insult," the Abbot said. "I only spoke of the malicious rumors of my wealth."

"Nevertheless," King John said, "I do not like your manner of speaking. You should be punished. Yet I will give you a chance to save your life. If you can answer three questions to my satisfaction I will spare you. If you fail, you have an appointment with the executioner."

Since he saw that he had no choice, the Abbot of Canterbury agreed to try.

"Here are the questions," the King said.

"First, tell me to an exact penny what I am worth.

"Second, tell me how soon I may ride the whole world about.

"And third, tell me exactly what I am thinking.

"If you cannot answer these questions, the headsman is waiting for you."

The Abbot was very discouraged, since for all his knowledge he could not answer a single one of the questions. But he begged the King to give him three weeks to find the answers, and the King granted him the time.

The Abbot rode away downcast in spirit. He rode to Cambridge, and he rode to Oxford, but not one of the clever professors there could help him. At last, when only a few days more remained, he was going sadly home, and he met by the roadside the shepherd who tended his sheep.

"Welcome home, Lord Abbot," the shepherd cried. "What is the news from the court?"

"Sad news, shepherd," the Abbot replied. "I have only three more days to live. Unless I can find the answers to three questions the King has asked me, I will lose my head."

"I pray you, Lord Abbot, what are these questions?" the shepherd asked.

The Abbot of Canterbury told him. "First, I am to tell the King what he is worth to a penny. Then I am to tell him how soon he may ride the whole world about. And lastly, I must tell him what he is thinking."

"Then cheer up, Lord Abbot," the shepherd said. "Did you never hear that even a fool may teach a wise man wit? Lend me a horse, some of your clothes, and servants to attend me. I will ride to London in your place and answer the King's questions."

The Abbot was not very pleased that an ignorant shepherd could possibly be mistaken for him. And he was still less pleased to think that the shepherd might be able to answer questions that the Abbot could not. But he had little choice in the matter, so he agreed with the proposal. He gave the shepherd his clothing, his horse, money, and servants to accompany him. While the Abbot continued his way home, the shepherd, disguised as the Abbot, rode off to London.

King John received the supposed Abbot coldly, but he repeated his promise to spare his life if the three questions were answered correctly.

The next day the King was seated in his Chair of State, wearing his most luxurious purple robe and his jeweled crown. The nobles and attendants were all around, waiting for the spectacle. Outside waited a man dressed all in black, the executioner.

The shepherd, wearing the Abbot's clothes, was brought in. He bowed to the King and said, "I am ready, Sire."

191

The nobles grinned in expectation.

"Tell me first," the King said, "how much I am worth to a penny."

"Sire," the shepherd said, "that is easy. In this fair land the coin that we call a sovereign is worth twenty shillings. The coin that we call a crown is worth five shillings. A sovereign minus a crown is worth fifteen shillings. But you, Sire, are a sovereign, and, as can be plainly seen, you have a crown as well. Therefore you must be worth exactly twenty-five shillings."

King John was forced to laugh when he heard this display of wit. "I did not think I was worth so little," he said, "but I will accept your answer, as the arithmetic is incontestable. So now you may answer the second question, Lord Abbot. How soon may I ride the whole world about?"

"That also is easy, Your Grace," the shepherd replied. "You must rise with the sun and ride with him all day, never falling behind. If you keep up with him until he rises the next morning you will have ridden around the whole world in twenty-four hours."

The King laughed again and accepted the answer. "It is true," he said, "that this is the only way it could be done. But now you have the hardest question of all. Tell me what I am thinking at this very moment."

"That," said the shepherd, "is the easiest question of all. Your Majesty is thinking that I am the Abbot of Canterbury. But I am not the Abbot of Canterbury at all; I am merely his poor shepherd, here to ask mercy for my worthy master."

And the shepherd quickly removed the garments he was

wearing.　Everyone saw that he was, in truth, not the Abbot of Canterbury.

The lords and courtiers roared with laughter.　King John frowned, for he did not relish being the object of a deception. But soon he joined in and laughed with the others.

The more he laughed, the more pleased he was with the entertainment.　So, in the end, he gave the Abbot a pardon and the shepherd a rich present for himself.

BUKOLLA
[*Iceland*]

Once upon a time a peasant and his wife lived with their son in a little farmhouse. Their only livestock was a cow called Bukolla.

The cow calved, and the peasant's wife herself sat up with it. As soon as the cow had recovered, the wife went back to the farmhouse. She came out again shortly afterwards to see how the cow was, but it had disappeared. Both the peasant and his wife started to hunt for the cow; they searched far and wide for a long time, but without success. They were very cross and ordered their son to go off and not to let them set eyes on him again until he came back with the cow. They fitted him out with new shoes and a store of provisions, and he set off without much idea of where to go.

After walking for a long, long time, he sat down to eat, and said, "Bukolla, moo now if you are alive anywhere." Then he heard Bukolla mooing far, far away.

Again he walked for a long, long time, and again he sat down to eat and said, "Bukolla, moo now if you are alive anywhere." Then he heard Bukolla moo a little closer than before.

Once more he walked for a long, long time, until he came to the top of a very high cliff. Once more he sat down to eat and said, "Bukolla, moo now if you are alive anywhere."

This time he heard the cow moo right underneath him. He climbed down the cliff until he came to a very big cave. He went inside the cave and there he found Bukolla tied to a beam. Untying her, he led her out behind him and set off for home.

When he had gone some distance, he saw an enormous giantess coming after him, and a smaller one with her. The big giantess was taking such long strides that he could tell that she would catch up with him in no time. So he asked, "What are we to do now, Bukolla?"

Bukolla answered, "Take a hair out of my tail and lay it on the ground."

He did so; then Bukolla said to the hair, "I solemnly pronounce this spell: you shall turn into a river so great that nothing can cross it but a bird on the wing." Instantly the hair turned into a vast river.

When the giantess came to the river she said, "That's not going to help you, my lad. Dash home, lass, and fetch my father's big bull." The smaller giantess went off and came back with a huge bull, which promptly drank up the whole river.

Then the peasant's son again saw that the giantess would catch up with him directly, because she took such big strides. So again he asked, "What are we to do now, Bukolla?"

"Take a hair out of my tail and lay it on the ground," Bukolla replied. And when he had done so, Bukolla said to the hair, "I solemnly pronounce this spell: you shall turn into a blaze so fierce that no one can get over it but a bird on the wing." And at once the hair turned into a blaze of fire.

When the giantess came to the fire she said, "That's not going to help you, my lad. Go and fetch my father's big bull, lass." The smaller giantess again went off and came back with the bull, which put out the fire with all the water it had drunk out of the river.

The peasant's son now saw once more that the giantess would soon catch him up, because she took such long strides. So once more he asked, "What are we to do now, Bukolla?" and once more Bukolla replied, "Take a hair out of my tail and lay it on the ground." Then Bukolla said to the hair, "I solemnly pronounce this spell: you shall turn into a mountain so big that no one can cross it but a bird on the wing."

Thereupon the hair turned into a mountain so high that the peasant's son could see nothing over it except clear sky.

When the giantess came to the mountain, she said, "That's not going to help you, my lad. Fetch my father's big gimlet, my lass!" The smaller giantess went away and came back with the gimlet. The big giantess then bored a hole in the mountain, but once she was able to see through it she became too impatient. She squeezed herself into the hole, but it was too narrow, so that she stuck fast and finally turned to stone, and there she remains to this day.

The peasant's son reached home safely with Bukolla, and his parents were overjoyed.

THE AMERICAS

THE DEER AND THE JAGUAR
SHARE A HOUSE
[*Brazil—An Indian Tale*]

One day a deer was wandering along a riverbank, and he said: "I have led a hard life, wandering here and there, never having a house of my own. I would like to have a house, and where would I ever find a better place than here? This is where I will build." And he went away.

A jaguar also said one day: "My life is full of trouble and cares. I shall look for a place to build a house, and I shall settle down comfortably." He went out to find a place, and he came to the same spot that the deer had chosen. When he saw it he exclaimed, "Wherever would I find a better spot for a house than this? Here is where I will live." And he went away, making plans to return.

The deer came back the following day to begin work on his house. It was great labor, but he cleared the ground of brush and trees and made it smooth and clean. Then he left, to return when he could.

The next day the jaguar came to begin work on his house, and he saw that the ground had already been cleared. "Ah!" he said. "The God Tupan is helping me with my work! What good fortune!" So he went to work on the floor of the house, and when the floor was finished it was nearly night and the jaguar went away.

The following morning the deer came and saw the floor

completed. He said, "Ah, the God Tupan is helping me build my house! What good luck!" And he built the walls of the house and returned to the forest.

The next day the jaguar came again and saw the walls finished. "Thank you, Tupan!" he said, and he put on the roof. Then he went back to the forest.

When the deer came back, he found the roof was finished. He said, "Thank you, Tupan, for all your help!" And in gratitude to the God Tupan, the deer made two rooms in the house, one for Tupan and one for himself. Then he entered one of the rooms and went to sleep.

That night the jaguar came once more. He went into the empty room to sleep, thinking he was sharing the house with Tupan, who had helped him build.

In the morning the deer and the jaguar got up at the same time. The jaguar asked in surprise, "Is it you who helped me build?"

The deer said, "Yes, is it you who helped me build?"

The jaguar said, "Yes. Since we have built this house together, let us share it."

The deer agreed, and they lived together, one in one room, the other in the other room.

One day the jaguar said, "I am going out hunting. I will bring food, so get everything ready, the pots, the water, and the wood for a fire."

He went out in the forest, while the deer prepared for the cooking. The jaguar killed a deer in the forest and brought it back. When the deer who was sharing the house saw what the food was, he became very sad. The jaguar cooked the food, but the deer wouldn't eat. After the jaguar had had his supper, they went to bed. But the deer was thinking with horror about the jaguar's diet, and he couldn't sleep. He feared that the jaguar would come in the night and eat him also.

In the morning the deer said to the jaguar, "Get the pots and the water and the wood ready. I am going hunting."

He went out in the forest and he saw another jaguar there sharpening his claws on the bark of a tree. The deer went on until he found an anteater, known as tamandua. He said to the tamandua, "The jaguar over there has been saying evil things about you."

When the tamandua heard this he became angry. He went to where the jaguar was and, creeping up silently behind him, seized him and killed him. Then he went away.

The deer took the carcass of the jaguar and carried it home. The pots and the water and the wood were ready. But when the jaguar with whom he was living saw what the deer had brought, he lost his appetite. Though the deer cooked the food, the jaguar couldn't eat a thing.

That night, neither the deer nor the jaguar could sleep. The jaguar feared that the deer might come for jaguar meat, and the deer feared that the jaguar would come for deer meat. They lay silently awake as the hours passed. When it was very late, they began to nod. In spite of his nervousness, the jaguar's eyes began to close a little. And so did the deer's. Suddenly the deer's eyes closed completely for a moment, and his head nodded. As he nodded, his antlers hit the wall with a loud noise.

When the jaguar heard the noise he awoke in fright, thinking the deer was coming after him, and he screamed.

When the deer heard the scream he was terrified, thinking the jaguar was coming to get him. Both animals leaped to their feet and fled from the house into the forest, one going in one direction and one in another.

And since that time, the jaguar and the deer have never lived together.

KAKUÍ, BIRD OF THE NIGHT
[*Argentina*]

Long ago, on the outskirts of the great forests of the north, a brother and sister lived together in a small thatched hut. As for the boy, his only thought was for the comfort and happiness of his sister. Every morning he would go off into the fields or forests to find something that would please her. He would search for wild fruit or he would fish in the streams and lakes, or he would climb tall trees to find honeycombs, and when he had found something good he would bring it home and give it to his sister. But the girl seemed not to care that her brother was doing so much for her. She repaid his affection only with unkindness. When he brought her a hard-won gift, she accepted it with scorn and contempt. Perhaps she would take a single bite of a fruit he had found for her, and then she would throw it away without concern for the effort it had cost him.

Sometimes he would spend the whole day fishing, standing waist-deep in the cold water; but when he came home wet and tired his sister wouldn't even look at the fish he had brought. Instead, she would scream at him and make his life a misery. His kindness to her received no thanks. The only words she ever spoke to him were sharp and cruel. If he returned with empty hands from a day of searching and asked for water to drink, she would bring it; but as he stretched his hand out to take it she would pour it on the ground, laughing at the look of surprise in his eyes. Only when she had played some cruel trick on her brother did the girl laugh. At other times, she spoke bitter and angry words, and she never stopped berating him.

For a long time the boy only increased his efforts, thinking that if he could bring his sister more wonderful presents from the forest she would return his affection. But nothing changed.

One day he went into a new part of the forest, pushing through brambles and thorns until his skin was torn and bleeding. At last he found a tall tree and saw a large swarm of bees hovering around it. He climbed and found a large sweet honeycomb. The bees attacked him and stung him, but he dug out the honeycomb with his knife, thinking that here at last he had something that would please his sister.

When he arrived home it was already night. His skin was covered with cuts and scratches from the thorns. His face and arms were swelled from the bee stings he had suffered. But when he gave his sister the honeycomb she despised it and threw it on the ground. When he asked for water to drink and wash his wounds, she brought it and threw it, also, on the ground, laughing at the look on his face.

Suddenly the boy understood what he had never understood before. He looked around the small house and saw how dirty and uncared-for it was. In the morning he went out and saw how the garden had dried up and wasted away because his sister had refused to water it. He saw how thin and hungry the animals were because his sister didn't feed them. He realized for the first time that his sister was a cruel and selfish creature, and that all his affection for her had been wasted.

His feeling of love turned to bitterness, and he made a plan to avenge himself. One morning he said, "I have found a wonderful present for you in the forest, a beautiful orchid, the largest I have ever seen."

"Go and get it for me then," the girl answered.

"No," the boy said, "it is something that you must come and see for yourself."

Her curiosity was aroused, and the girl went into the forest with him. He brought her to a tall tree and said, "This is the tree we must climb. You go up first and I will follow."

The girl went up first, and the brother followed with his ax. All the way up the girl scolded, saying, "I am sure it is ugly. I shall not like it." And when she was halfway up she said, "I don't see it."

"You must go higher," the boy said. And they continued to climb. At last the girl was at the very top.

"There is nothing here at all!" the girl screamed at her brother.

But there was no answer. She looked down and saw that her brother was climbing to the ground, chopping off all the branches as he went. There was no way for her to go down. She was stranded in the top of the tall tree in the middle of the forest. She saw her brother going away, and in a few minutes she was alone.

As she clung there in the treetop, waving and screaming, something began to happen. Feathers began to sprout all over her. Her feet turned into claws, and her nose turned into a beak.

"*Turay, Turay!*" she screamed. "Brother, brother!" But her brother was gone.

The girl had turned into a bird. So filled with shame was she, that she hid in the forest during the daytime and left it only at night. She became known as Kakuí, bird of the night, and to this day she can be heard in the great forests of the north, crying, "*Turay! Turay!* Brother! Brother!"

THE COMING OF ASIN
[*Bolivia—An Indian Legend*]

There was once a chief among the Pilagá people by the
name of Nalaraté. Nalaraté was known for his victories in
war, and the men who followed him were battle-hardened
warriors. Into Nalaraté's village one day there came a curious stranger. When the people saw him they laughed, for
he was grotesque and ugly. Whereas other men were lean
and straight, the stranger was crooked and his belly was large.
And whereas other men had long black hair, the stranger
had none at all. Other men wore loincloths, but as for the
stranger, he wore a fox-skin cloak over his shoulders.

"What kind of creature is this?" Nalaraté's people asked
each other. "He is not of the Toba tribe, nor of the Matacao, nor the Tereno. He must be a tribe all by himself,
for where could there be other people like him?" They
mocked him this way, but the stranger simply listened and
made no answer. Finally one of the Pilagá asked him,
"Who are you?"

"My name is Asin," the stranger answered quietly.

He remained in the village and built himself a small
shelter of boughs and grass. The people tolerated him as
a curiosity, and they treated him as a beggar. If a man
caught a fish that was too small to cook, he might toss it
to Asin, and Asin would take it humbly and express his
thanks. But though the people didn't send Asin out of the

village they abused him in many ways. Sometimes, for sport, the men would wipe their hands on Asin's fox-skin cloak and make a great joke of it when he complained.

One day Asin went to the house of the chief. Nalaraté said, "Do not enter here. What is in my house that you want to steal?"

Asin answered, "I only want to borrow a comb from your daughter."

Nalaraté laughed. "Since you have no hair on your head, what could you do with a comb?"

But Nalaraté's daughter overheard them talking, and she said to Asin, "Here, I will lend you the comb."

Asin took it and thanked her and went down to the river. The girl picked up her water jars and followed him, curious as to what he would do with a comb. When she came near the river, she hid among the trees and watched Asin. She saw him remove his fox-skin cloak. As Asin stood there in the water he changed instantly into a handsome young warrior with long black hair, which he combed with the comb the girl had lent him.

"He is handsome and he has great powers!" the girl said to herself. "I will have him for my husband."

Asin finished combing his hair. Then he transformed himself again into the ugly stranger, and put the fox-skin cloak back on his shoulders. After he had left, the girl filled her water jars and carried them home.

When Asin came to Nalaraté's house to return the comb, the girl said, "Sit down with me here."

Asin replied, "Why do you want me to sit with you? I am ugly."

The girl said, "Even though my father will object, I will have you for my husband."

Asin answered, "Very well, then. Let us sit outside where people can see."

The girl put a skin on the ground in front of the house and they sat on it together, signifying that they were married. When people saw them sitting there, they said, "The chief's daughter has lost her mind. She is married to Asin."

When Nalaraté came he was angry. He ordered his daughter to leave Asin and choose another man of the village, but she refused, saying, "He is my husband now."

That night, Asin demonstrated his magic powers. From under the fox-skin cloak he brought out a mosquito netting to protect them from insects. He brought out food, and they ate. He brought out a beautiful red skirt-cloth and gave it to his wife.

When the girl's mother saw what Asin could do, she said, "I didn't protest when you married Asin. What can he bring out from under the fox skin for me?"

The girl said, "Ask for what you want, he will give it to you."

The mother said, "It is the beautiful red skirt-cloth that I want."

"Take it," Asin said, and she took it. Then Asin reached under the fox-skin cloak and brought out a yellow skirt-cloth for his wife. He brought out ears of corn and a honeycomb full of honey and gave them to the girl's mother, and she was grateful. She said again, "I wasn't one of those who objected to Asin's living here."

Nalaraté was at a drinking party with the warriors of the

village. When he returned early in the morning he said, "Get my things ready, we are going on an expedition against the Matacao tribe."

Asin said, "I will come with you."

The chief replied scornfully, "No, how could I take you? You would be a hindrance. You are no warrior. You don't even have a horse. If you had a horse, could you even make it go in the right direction? And if you arrived at the place of battle, what could you do but cause us shame and misery? No, stay here with the women. As for my daughter, she chose a beggar instead of a warrior. She will starve. I will give her nothing."

Nalaraté and his warriors mounted their horses and rode away. When they were out of sight, Asin said, "Now I will go."

He mounted his donkey and followed the war party. When he had left the village behind, he clapped his hands together, *tao*, and his donkey changed into a fiery iron horse. He clapped his hands again, *tao*, and changed himself into a handsome young man as his wife had seen him at the river. When night came, Nalaraté's warriors made camp. Before Asin entered the camp, he changed his iron horse back into a donkey, and himself into an ugly man without hair.

The war party saw him then, and they made jokes and asked, "Why did you come?" They threw him some scraps of food, which he took. After a while he mounted his donkey and rode on ahead of the war party. He spent the night alone at a watering place. He brought out food from under his fox skin and he ate until he was satisfied.

In the morning he again joined the warriors, and he rode

at a distance behind them. The men joked about Asin. Then they sighted the camp of the enemy. Nalaraté ordered Asin to return to the village. He said, "Go back at once before you cause us trouble and shame."

Asin stopped and waited, as the Pilagá men went cautiously forward. Then he changed himself into the warrior with the flowing black hair, and he changed his donkey into the fiery iron horse. He rode fiercely past the Pilagá men into the camp of the enemy and fought with them. Nalaraté's warriors stopped and watched the battle, asking each other, "Who is this man? Who is this man?"

One of them cried out, "It is Asin! He changed his donkey into a fiery iron horse!"

Then the Pilagá went forward to join the battle, but by the time they arrived Asin had scattered the enemy and rounded up all the horses. They met him coming back, driving the horses before him. He did not speak to the Pilagá, but went on and left them behind.

Asin returned to the village. He said to his wife, "Let us leave this village where I have been mistreated." His wife agreed. Her mother said, "I will come too." So Asin took them and his horses to a new place on the edge of a river and made a new house.

When Nalaraté arrived home he found his house empty. The women of the village told him how Asin had gone away with his household.

The men blamed Nalaraté, saying, "It is your fault, you abused him. And he is the greatest of warriors."

Nalaraté was angry. He said, "If you want him for your chief, follow him."

Many of the men did. They took their families and went to the place where Asin had built his house. There they built a new village. And Asin was the chief.

Nalaraté decided he would destroy Asin for the grief he had caused him. But Asin learned of the plot, and he called all the men of the village together and spoke to them. He said, "There is a wind coming. It will be cold. Go and brace your houses, and put heavy thatch on the roof." They went and prepared their houses. Then Asin clapped his hands, *tao*, and the cold wind came. It swept across the country. People became cold and sought refuge inside their houses. But the wind blew away the thatch from the roofs. Only in Asin's village did the roofs remain. Everywhere else people were punished by the cold and the wind. In his own house Asin clapped his hands, *tao*, and made a fire. People came to him begging for an ember so that they could have a fire in their houses too. To those people who were his friends, Asin gave firebrands. When his enemies came and begged for fire, he turned them away. Nalaraté himself came, but Asin said, "First you merely abused me; then you planned to kill me. Why should I give you fire?" Nalaraté went away and was cold.

All those who hadn't abused Asin had fire and were warm, but the others suffered and died. The rivers froze, and snow covered the land.

At last the wind stopped, and the ice and snow melted, and Asin came out of his house. He went to Nalaraté's village and found the people dead. He changed the old men into yulo birds and mazamorras birds, and they flew away. He changed the old women into chaja birds, and they flew away. He changed the middle-aged people into hawks and vultures, and they flew away. And the children, he changed into ducks and herons, and they flew away. Asin found Nalaraté where he had taken refuge from the cold in a well, and he changed him into an alligator.

This is the legend of Asin, who was abused because of his appearance.

THE LEGEND OF THE CHINGOLO BIRD
[Paraguay]

In the language of the Guarani Indians the Chingolo bird is known as *Che sy asy*, meaning "My mother is sick." It is called *Che sy asy* because that is what it sings when the wind is about to change and blow from the south, bringing with it bad weather and bitter cold. People listen with respect to the call of the Chingolo. For it warns them to drive their sheep from the pastures to the pens, and to seek shelter for themselves. Hardly ever is the Chingolo wrong, and people are grateful to him for his help.

In early days there was no Chingolo bird, but a Guarani boy named Chingolo. It happened one day that Chingolo's mother became very sick. There was only one cure for her illness, a certain herb which grew among the great trees of the forest. Knowing that she would surely die if she could not have this medicine, she asked Chingolo to go and find it for her.

Though the forest was dark, and though the jaguar and other dangerous wild creatures lived there, Chingolo went in search of the plant. Though he was afraid, he loved his mother dearly, and he didn't hesitate. He came to the forest and entered it, searching among the great trees for the medicine he knew he must find.

Chingolo wandered far, looking everywhere. He heard the cries of the jaguar, but he went on. At last, among the dense moss and ferns, he found the plant he was looking for. He dug it out of the earth and wrapped it in leaves. Then he started for home.

But darkness comes early in the forest. And soon the night was around him, and he couldn't find the trail by which he had come. He wandered this way and that, holding the medicine plant tightly in his arms.

When the morning dawned and the light came again, Chingolo knew he was lost. Time and time again he called out for help, saying: *"Che sy asy! Che sy asy!*—My mother is sick! My mother is sick!" But no one heard, and Chingolo wandered on, looking for a way out of the forest. Night came again. Chingolo was cold and hungry. When day came once more, it was the same as before.

And while Chingolo wandered this way, lost in the forest, his mother died.

Thus no one knew where Chingolo was except the gods. So that Chingolo would not be a lost orphan, the gods changed him into a bird. From that day onward, he flew from place to place, seeking the spirit of his mother. Sometimes he is seen in the forest, sometimes he makes his nest under the eaves of the village houses. And when he knows the bitter cold wind is coming, he warns the villagers by crying out:

"Che sy asy! Che sy asy!—My mother is sick! My mother is sick!"

THE ORIGIN OF THE CAMLET FLOWER
[*Uruguay*]

Everywhere in Uruguay is to be found a lovely blue water plant called the Camlet flower.   Wherever there is water, whether it be a pond, a river, or a lake, the lovely Camlet flower is likely to be seen floating there.   But it is said that there was not always a Camlet flower.   And here is the legend of its origin:

Once, in the old days, a peaceful tribe of Indians lived on the bank of a river.   They hunted and fished for food and made their clothes from animal skins.   Life was good to them.   And then, one day, strange, light-skinned people from another land invaded the country.   They took over the hunting grounds of the Indians and made farms.   They built houses and forts.   Where the Indians had lived peacefully, the light-skinned strangers settled down to stay.   The Indians fought to keep their hunting grounds and their fishing waters.   Although their weapons were only the arrow, the spear, and the bola, and though the strangers had rifles and gunpowder, the Indians won many battles.   But in the end they could not hold out against the power of the invaders.

They retreated from the lands they had owned and settled on new camp sites.   But in time the fighting ceased, and the Indians and the white people learned to live in friendship as neighbors.

Old people say that there was a girl in the village of the

strangers, the daughter of the white chief. She was remarkable for her beauty and her kindness, and she came to be loved by the Indians.

It happened once that Indian children were playing in the river. Unexpectedly, the waters began to rise. A torrent of water from the hills rushed down through the riverbed, overrunning the banks, and sweeping before it trees and houses. The children scrambled to the shore, all except one little Indian boy who was caught in the current. Hearing the shouts of the other children, the daughter of the white village chief came running to the scene, and she saw the boy floundering in the deep rushing water. Others came running too, but the girl didn't wait. She flung herself into the river to save the drowning child. She reached him and kept him afloat, but she was too tired to bring him back to the shore. Her father, the white chief, plunged into the water also. He swam to where they were struggling against the current, took the boy and brought him safely to the riverbank. But before he could return for his daughter, she was swept away and sank from sight beneath the swirling water.

There was great sorrow in the white village and in the Indian camps. The father of the girl could not be consoled.

And then one day the Indians came to him with a message from their god Tupá. Tupá had been deeply moved by the girl's sacrifice for the boy, and he ordained that she should live on in another form—a flower that would always be seen on the surface of the rivers and the lakes.

So it is that the Camlet flower is seen every spring, its blossom as blue as the eyes of the gentle girl on whom Tupá bestowed immortality.

THE FIVE EGGS

[*Ecuador*]

In the fields near the city there lived two poor peasants, named Juan and Juanica. Since they were very poor they would sometimes go two or even three days without eating.

Once after they had had nothing to eat for three days, Juanica asked her husband, "How long are we going to keep on living if we don't eat?"

"Don't worry," he said, "I will go to town today to see if I can manage to find money to buy five eggs for us to boil and eat."

Immediately he set out for town. On arrival, he stood on a corner to wait for a passer-by from whom he could ask alms. When he saw a man coming, he said to him, "Listen, my friend! Would you be good enough to give me four cents to buy an egg?" And the man, who was very charitable, gave him the four cents. That happened five times, and the peasant was fortunate enough not to have one of the five refuse him. When he had enough to buy the five eggs, he went on and bought them. And then he returned home to tell his wife the good news.

When he arrived, he told his wife to boil the eggs at once, for he was so hungry he could eat a burro. When the eggs were all boiled, his wife said to him, "Juan, come eat your two eggs; I shall eat three because I cooked them."

But he immediately said no, that he was the one to have the three eggs, and she should have only two. And he kept on insisting, saying, "Three for me and two for you." But his wife was stubborn, maintaining that she was to have three and he two. And that went on and on.

After they had wasted a good deal of time talking, Juanica decided to tell Juan that if he did not give her the three eggs to eat she would die. But he said to her, very indifferently, "All right, that makes no difference to me. Go ahead and die!"

So she fell to the ground as though dead. Then he began to weep, "Oh, my poor wife, I loved her so. Oh, my poor wife!" And after he had wept until he was tired, he whispered in her ear, "Juanica, don't be so silly. I'll eat three and you two." But she answered, "No, I am going to eat three and you two, or else you can bury me." So he kept on weeping.

After he saw that his wife refused to come to life again, he decided to go and look for his best friends. He had five friends, and when he reached their homes he told them that he had come to ask them please to bury his wife, who had just died, and that he was counting on them, for he did not have a single cent to buy a casket. So his friends said not to worry, that they would see to that.

On his return home, he found her still playing dead. Then Juan burst into tears again, "Oh, Juanica, do not leave me alone, please!" And when no one was looking he slipped near where she lay to whisper in her ear, "I am going to eat three and you two." But she said no, that she was going to eat the three and he two. Then he said to her, "Take care, for we are going to bury you." And she replied, "That's nothing; bury me whenever you like."

After waiting a good while, they put her in the casket to carry her to the cemetery. And on the way Juan kept on crying, "Oh, my poor wife, don't leave me!" And he made them stop the funeral procession, supposedly to kiss her, but really to tell her that he was going to eat three and she two. But her reply was always the same. When they reached the cemetery, they bore her to the edge of the grave. Then he went up to her and whispered in her ear, "Look, you are on the edge of the grave, and we are about to put you in it." Then, when she realized he was telling the truth, she sat up in the casket and said, "All right, then; you can eat all five of them."

So she got up out of the casket and they both went home.

But once arrived there, Juanica set the five eggs on the table—and ate three.

THE MAGIC SANDALS OF HUALACHI
[Peru]

In the ancient days of the Incas of Tahuantinsuyo (now called Peru), an Emperor named Huiracocha had, as was the custom, many messengers. These men, called *chasquis*, were renowned for their endurance and their speed. When the ruler of the Incas wished to send a message to some part of his vast kingdom, his ministers would prepare a *quipu*, made of knotted cords of different colors. Then a messenger would take the *quipu* and run with it along the stone-paved roads, until he came to a rest station. Here another messenger would take the *quipu* and carry it further. In this way, messages were sent to government officials hundreds of miles away in an incredibly short time.

Among the messengers of Huiracocha there was a man by the name of Hualachi. He was brave and intelligent, loyal to his ruler, and a courageous runner. But Hualachi had one weakness—he was easily distracted by the sight of suffering. Often when carrying a *quipu* for his ruler he would see some hurt creature near the road, and he could not refrain from stopping to help the animal, quite forgetful that somewhere along the highway other messengers were waiting in relays for the *quipu* he carried. The ruler of the Incas knew about Hualachi's weakness, but he loved his messenger because Hualachi had once saved him from great danger at the risk of his own life.

One day Huiracocha called Hualachi and gave him a *quipu* to bring to the chief of the Inca armies, which were holding back a warlike enemy on the frontier. The *quipu* contained instructions for the Inca soldiers. Huiracocha warned Hualachi not to tarry by the wayside, but to go with all speed to his destination.

Hualachi promised to do so, and he set out. But on the way he heard a pitiful cry from the bottom of a ravine near the road, and looking down he saw an old woman who had fallen down the steep slope. Forgetting the message he carried, Hualachi went down into the ravine. He found that the old woman had broken her leg. He picked her up and carried her on his back to her mountain house, and there he looked after her until she could walk a little and take care of herself again.

Many days had passed since Hualachi had set out with his message, which he had completely forgotten. But he discovered the *quipu* in his belt, and suddenly remembered his errand. He began to run toward the distant frontier, as fast as he could go. He ran faster than he ever had run before, and he didn't stop to rest even though his heart pounded and his lungs cried for air. But long before he reached the frontier he met another *chasqui* coming in the opposite direction, running towards Cuzco.

"There is no need to go any further," the other messenger said. "The battle is over. This is the message I am carrying to Huiracocha."

"Have we been defeated?" Hualachi asked in great distress, sure that his carelessness had caused a disaster.

"No," the other messenger said. "We were victorious.

When you left the road to aid the old woman, someone saw you and reported it to Huiracocha. He sent another messenger in your place."

So Hualachi went back to Cuzco, full of shame and remorse. He told Huiracocha what he had done and asked forgiveness. But the Inca ruler replied that there was no choice, he would have to send Hualachi away.

So Hualachi left Cuzco and wandered through the countryside, going from place to place aimlessly. And one day he came to a temple of Pachacámac, the Creator. He threw himself on the ground before the temple and asked Pachacámac for help. He poured out his misery at having failed his trust.

Then Hualachi heard a voice. It said, "Take heart. Huiracocha is as sad as you are that you have left him. Go back to Cuzco, and he will take you again as one of his *chasquis.* As a messenger you may have failed, but I know that you have done many good deeds and I will help you."

"But how can I be sure I will not fail Huiracocha again?" Hualachi said. "For I am so easily distracted from my tasks!"

"Look on the earth beside you," the voice of Pachacámac said.

Hualachi looked, and he saw there a pair of sandals.

"With these sandals on your feet," the voice of Pachacámac went on, "you have only to wish to be in a certain place and you will be transported there like a flash of lightning. In this way, there will be no more distractions along the road."

Hualachi put on the sandals and wished to be back in

Cuzco. In an instant he was there. Huiracocha was delighted to see him, and Hualachi asked to be reinstated as a royal *chasqui.* "Oh Huiracocha," he said, "no more will my thoughts wander when I carry your *quipu.* And I shall prove to you that I am now the swiftest of your messengers."

The ruler of the Incas smiled and said, "We shall see. Tomorrow we shall arrange a competition among six of the swiftest messengers in my service. You too will run."

The next day Hualachi and the other *chasquis* set out together, each carrying a *quipu* bearing a different message to a governor of a distant province. Hualachi ran with the others until he was out of sight of Cuzco, and after that he slowed his pace and dropped behind. And when there was a great distance between them, he put on his sandals and wished. In an instant he was at his destination, where he delivered his message and received the governor's reply.

He set out on foot then, on the return journey to Cuzco. And on the road he met the other messengers running wearily toward the governor's house. They were astounded to see Hualachi already on the way back. He said nothing apart from his greeting, and when he had passed them and was alone he put on his sandals and was transported like lightning to the house of the Inca ruler.

Huiracocha was elated at Hualachi's success, and installed him as the chief of all the *chasquis.* Never before had there been a messenger as swift as he, nor has there been one since. The speed with which he carried out his missions for the ruler of the Incas gave him much leisure, which he devoted to alleviating the sufferings of human beings and animals alike.

HOW LIFE AND LIGHT CAME
INTO THE WORLD
[Colombia—A Chibcha Creation Myth]

In the beginning there was no light. Everything was in darkness. The earth was soft and cold, and nothing grew. There was neither vegetation, nor animal life, nor beauty. Everything was desolate. There were no people. The only living creatures on earth were the god Nemequene, his wife, and his son.

Nemequene sought to create life and beauty on the earth. Out of the soft, cold mud, he fashioned the figures of people and animals. Day after day he worked at the task. But the figures he made were lifeless. They neither moved nor breathed. The years went by, and still there were only Nemequene and his family.

At last Nemequene called his son, and he sent him up into the sky to give light. Nemequene's son went into the sky and became Súa, the sun. Suddenly the dark world was illuminated. Súa's brilliant rays flooded the land. The cold mud became warm. Grass, trees, and plants began to grow. Where there had been only dark desolation, the world turned lush and green. Water began to flow, and there were rivers and lakes.

And the warm sunlight brought life into the mud figures which Nemequene had made. Some of them became birds, which flew up and nested in the trees of the forests; some became fish, which went into the water; some became animals; and some became humans.

Yet the people created by Nemequene were not altogether happy, for the light and warmth which Súa shed on them came only part of the time. Each night, while Súa rested, there was darkness. The people went to Nemequene and asked him to help them.

Nemequene loved the people whom he had created, and he wanted to help them. So he too went up into the sky and became Chía, the moon. He shared the task of giving light to the world with his son Súa. Súa cast his rays on the earth in the daytime, and Chía at night. From that time on, the people created by Nemequene were contented. They never forgot to give thanks.

They held feasts in honor of Súa and Chía, and sometimes they dedicated their children to the sun and the moon. Such children were known as Suachias long before they had names of their own.

Thus it was that life came into the world, and that the Chibchas—the people of Nemequene—remembered how it happened.

THE SINGING FLUTE

[Venezuela]

There was once a King with three sons named Pedro, Juan, and José. It happened one time that the King's eyesight began to fail. Little by little he was becoming blind. The best physicians in the country came, but they could do nothing for him.

At last one doctor told him, "There is a cure for this sickness of your eyes. The remedy is a medicine distilled from the flower of the olive tree."

When the King heard this he was glad. But then he thought, "Wherever will I get the flower of the olive tree? For there are no olive trees in this country."

In despair he sent for his three sons and told them about the medicine which could be made if only an olive blossom could be found. And he asked them to help him.

Then the oldest son, Pedro, said to his father, "I will go and look for an olive flower. But it will be expensive to go here and there. Give me my inheritance now, and I will begin the search."

So the king gave Pedro his inheritance, and Pedro went out to find an olive tree. He traveled far, and on the road he met an old woman begging for charity. But Pedro was not of a generous nature, and he refused to give her anything. He continued his journey with a single purpose, to find an olive tree in blossom. The weeks and months went by. He found nothing.

Anxious because his oldest son failed to return, the King called his second son, Juan, and asked him also to go out and seek an olive flower. Juan asked his father for half his inheritance, and he went out searching. On the road he too met the old woman begging alms. Like Pedro he refused her and continued his way. He went here and there, scanning the landscape with his eyes, but he found no olive trees. More weeks passed. When the youngest son José saw that neither of his brothers returned, and that his father's eyes were getting worse every day, he went to the King and said, "Give me your blessing, father, and I will try to find the olive blossom which will restore your sight."

The king gave José his blessing, and the young man began his journey. He traveled far, and on the road he too met the old woman who asked for charity. He was filled with compassion for her poverty, and he said, "I have no money to give you, but I will gladly share my food." He opened his knapsack and gave her half of what was in it. The two of them sat and ate together, and he told the old woman of his search.

She said, "Wherever will anyone find olive trees in this country?"

José nodded in agreement. But when the woman had finished eating she said, "I will tell you where there are olive trees. Many miles to the west is a mountain which rises up from the floor of the valley. High up on the east slope of this mountain is a grove of olive trees. There you will find your blossoms."

They parted then, and José went westward until he came to the mountain that rose from the floor of the valley. And there on the eastern slope he found an olive grove in bloom. He joyfully picked some olive flowers and quickly began his journey homeward.

On the way he met his brothers, who had searched for the olive flower in vain. Rather than being glad that José had been successful, they were jealous of his accomplishment. They took the blossoms away from him, and when he protested they beat him so hard that he fell on the ground quiet and motionless. Fearful of their wicked act being discovered, they buried José by the roadside and hurried home.

The King rejoiced when Pedro and Juan returned with the olive blossoms. The King's sight was restored, and great honors were bestowed on the two sons. But the continued absence of José filled the King with anxiety and grief.

On the spot where Juan and Pedro had buried their brother a strange thing happened. Out of the earth which covered him, reeds began to sprout. One day a shepherd was passing by, and he heard a sweet musical sound coming from the reeds. He approached closely and listened. He heard a young voice singing:

> "Shepherd, play upon me
> And give me the power
> To tell the true, true story
> Of the magic olive flower."

So the shepherd cut one of the reeds and made a flute of it. When he placed the flute to his mouth to play, the same sweet words and music came out again. The shepherd went around the countryside with his flute, and everywhere the people heard the song:

"Play upon me
And give me the power
To tell the true story
Of the olive flower."

The fame of the flute spread far and wide. At last the King heard of the matter, and he sent for the shepherd so that he might hear this strange thing for himself. The shepherd came and stood before the King. He placed the flute to his lips and blew gently, and a young voice sang:

"Oh father, play upon me
And give me the power
To tell the true, true story
Of the magic olive flower."

The King seized the flute from the shepherd's hands. He placed it to his lips and blew upon it, and he heard José's young voice telling the story of how the olive blossoms were found, and how his brothers had beaten him and buried him by the roadside.

In grief and anguish, the King had Juan and Pedro thrown into prison, and he set out at once for the place where José was buried. His soldiers found the bed of reeds by the roadside, and they dug up the earth and found there the body of José. But the great miracle had not yet ended, for José was not dead, as his brothers had believed him to be.

He stood up and embraced his father, and the King wept for joy.

There were great celebrations at José's return.   And as a thanks-offering for the return of his sight and his youngest son, the King released Juan and Pedro from their imprisonment.

THE GOLDEN ALTAR OF
THE CHURCH OF ST. JOSEPH
[*Panama*]

In the Church of Saint Joseph, in the City of Panama, there is a golden altar more than three centuries old. It is more ancient than the church in which it stands, having survived the brigandage of the pirate Henry Morgan and the fire that destroyed the original city of Panama.

Three hundred years ago the altar stood in another Church of Saint Joseph. Word came to the city that the ship of Henry Morgan was on its way to loot the city of its treasures. The priests and brothers of the churches were advised to hide anything of value. But in the Church of Saint Joseph there was a problem. The beautiful golden altar was too large to hide anywhere. At last one of the brothers had an idea. He suggested that the altar should be painted and camouflaged to appear a worthless object. With the help of some of the people of Panama, the priests and brothers collected clay and herbs, and out of these things they made a crude kind of paint. Even as Henry Morgan was sailing into the harbor, they began to apply their paint to the golden altar. They worked all night and finished only as the sun was rising. In the first light of morning Henry Morgan's buccaneers came ashore, and it was only a matter of minutes before they were beating on the doors of the Church of Saint Joseph.

When they entered the church they went from room to room but found nothing of value—no money, no objects of silver or gold. Henry Morgan himself stood before the altar, and he saw an old priest, undisturbed by the invasion, touching up the altar with a little paint.

"That is a strange and ugly paint you are using," Henry Morgan said. "Why do you not use oil paint?"

The old priest stopped his work long enough to reply to the pirate. "We are a poor parish," he said. "We do not have money for such luxuries. The paint we are using was made with our own hands out of the very earth of Panama."

Then, it is said, Henry Morgan did an astonishing thing. He reached into his pocket and brought out a handful of silver, which he gave to the priest. "Take this," he said, "and buy oil paint for the church."

When Henry Morgan and his men had left the church, the priests, the brothers, and the townspeople fell on their knees and thanked God for saving their altar.

But the pirates continued to seek their loot elsewhere in the city. And that night as they retired to their ship, they put the city to the torch. The fire spread in all directions. It became a raging inferno. People fled for safety where they could. From the tower of the Church of Saint Joseph, the priests could see the approaching flames. There was nothing to do. They simply waited and prayed that the fire would burn itself out before it reached the church. When at last there was no further hope that the church would be spared, they placed a statue of Saint Joseph on the golden altar and, carrying what they could, went away.

The fire set by the pirate Henry Morgan burned down

most of the old city of Panama. When its fury was over, people came back to find smoldering ruins. They found that the Church of Saint Joseph had been partially destroyed. But the golden altar, covered with the crude and ugly paint made of earth, was untouched by the flames. And when, at last, the new Church of Saint Joseph was built, the golden altar was placed in it. And there it remains to this day.

UNCLE COYOTE'S LAST MISCHIEF
[*Nicaragua*]

Long ago, it is said, Uncle Coyote's mischief was known everywhere. He lived in the open fields and roamed around the outskirts of the town looking for choice morsels of food. Smaller creatures were afraid of Uncle Coyote because he was very clever and always hungry. But Uncle Rabbit wasn't afraid. Uncle Rabbit was clever too, and it was he who often persuaded Uncle Coyote to play mischievous jokes on others. Whenever something bad happened in the village, people would blame it on Uncle Coyote.

One day Uncle Coyote was sleeping under a mango tree. He was awakened by Uncle Rabbit, who said: "Wake up, Uncle Coyote, wake up! I have just been to the Padre's garden, and there is a beautiful ripe watermelon there!"

Uncle Coyote woke up at once, and his mouth began to water at the thought of a ripe melon. "Don't stand there, Uncle Rabbit," Uncle Coyote said. "Let's go and see the Padre's garden!"

They went along the hedge at the edge of the Padre's garden so that the housekeeper wouldn't see them. And when they came to the beautiful green watermelon, Uncle Rabbit whispered, "Let's eat it, Uncle Coyote!"

"Yes," Uncle Coyote replied, "let's eat it!" And with his sharp claws Uncle Coyote cut the melon in two. Then he began to eat one half and Uncle Rabbit began to eat the other half. Soon there was nothing left but the empty rind. Uncle Coyote was happy. But as they stood there licking their lips, they heard the Padre's housekeeper say, "Tonight we will have that ripe watermelon to eat."

Uncle Coyote said to Uncle Rabbit, "Ha, now see what trouble I am in! She will find the melon gone, and I will be blamed!"

"I have an idea," Uncle Rabbit said. "Let's fill the empty rind with mud and put the two halves back together again. The Padre's old housekeeper is very nearsighted; she'll never know the difference."

"A beautiful, clever idea!" Uncle Coyote said.

They filled the empty watermelon shells with mud and then stuck the two halves together, after which they scurried away. Uncle Coyote, full of watermelon, became sleepy, and he went back to his favorite spot to take a nap. As for Uncle Rabbit, he went back to the edge of the village to see what was going on. He watched the Padre's housekeeper come and take the melon from the garden. And after a while he heard a great commotion in the Padre's house. When the noise had subsided a little, Uncle Rabbit went into the kitchen. There he saw the old housekeeper carrying on. She was furious.

"What has happened that makes you so upset?" he asked.

"Ah, that Uncle Coyote! He not only ate the Padre's watermelon, but he filled the rind with mud! And when the Padre cut it open tonight his plate was filled with dirt! Oh, that good-for-nothing Coyote!"

"Well," Uncle Rabbit said, "I'll tell you what I'll do. I'll bring Uncle Coyote here tonight for you."

"Ah, Uncle Rabbit, you are so good!" the housekeeper said. "Here is a head of lettuce for you."

Uncle Rabbit took the lettuce and ate it, wondering how he'd manage to bring Coyote into the house.

All this time Uncle Coyote was sleeping. But he was suddenly awakened by the high-pitched singing of a cicada in a nearby tree. He was quite annoyed to have his sleep interrupted, so he got up and went to the tree and told the cicada to stop her singing. Uncle Coyote lay down again and closed his eyes. But the cicada kept singing in her high-pitched voice. Uncle Coyote came back angrily and told the cicada that if she didn't stop he would punish her. When Uncle Coyote lay down again, the cicada slipped out of her old dried-up skin, as cicadas do once every year. She put a stone inside the old skin and left it right on the branch where she had been sitting. Then she flew to another branch and began to sing even louder than before.

When Uncle Coyote heard the high-pitched sound of the cicada again, he was furious. He got up and ran back to the tree, shouting, "If you don't stop that noise at once I'll come up there and eat you!" But the cicada kept singing, and Uncle Coyote, losing the last shreds of his patience, leaped up and snapped at the old skin sitting on the branch. He bit very hard, and when his teeth closed on the stone inside, he was very surprised. There was a terrible ache in his mouth, and he discovered that some of his teeth were broken. Uncle Coyote rolled on the ground, howling with pain.

It was just at this moment that Uncle Rabbit found him. "My teeth, my teeth!" Uncle Coyote was moaning. That gave Uncle Rabbit an idea, and he said, "Let us go to the Padre's housekeeper. She will give you something for your toothache."

So Uncle Coyote hurried with Uncle Rabbit to the Padre's house. The minute they stepped into the kitchen, the housekeeper called out:

"Ah, Uncle Coyote, take that for eating the Padre's watermelon!" And she lighted Coyote's tail with a firebrand. Feeling pain in his tail as well as his teeth, Uncle Coyote turned and fled. He didn't even hear Uncle Rabbit shouting, "Good-by Uncle Coyote with the burned-out tail and the broken teeth!"

Uncle Coyote headed straight for the river, and when he arrived there he leaped into the water to cool down the pain. From that day to now, Uncle Coyote has been seen no more.

> *Adios, Tío Coyote*
> *Cola quemada*
> *Dientes quebrados!*
>
> Good-by Uncle Coyote
> With the burned-out tail
> And the broken teeth!

THE PEASANT AND THE HORSEMAN
[*Costa Rica*]

It happened one day that a poor Indian peasant was traveling on the road to Nicoya. He was going there to participate in the great festival of the Virgin of Guadalupe. But the distance from his village near the foot of Beautiful Mountain to Nicoya was long, and over his shoulder he carried a heavy bag of provisions for the trip. The bulging bag contained ripe plantains, mangos, dried fish, and other food. But the road was hot and dusty, and the Indian sat down in the shade of a tree to rest.

As he sat there, he saw a horse and rider coming along the road. When the rider came to the shade tree, he also stopped and allowed his horse to nibble at the grass. He nodded to the Indian and greeted him condescendingly. "Buenos dias," he said, and the peasant replied, "Buenos dias." The Indian looked at the rich man's sleek horse, thinking how good it would be to be able to ride with his heavy load.

"Where are you going, Señor?" the Indian asked in a friendly tone.

"To Nicoya," the horseman replied.

"Ah, this is a coincidence!" the peasant said. "I too am going to Nicoya for the festival of the Virgin of Guadalupe!"

The horseman shrugged his shoulders.

"Señor," the Indian said, "the road to Nicoya is long,

the sun is hot, and my bundle is very heavy. Would you let me ride with you on your horse for a few miles?"

The horseman looked at the Indian, then at his bundle. He shook his head and replied, "I regret that my horse could not possibly carry the two of us and your bundle as well."

The Indian took no offense at the refusal. He simply said, "Señor, if my heavy bag of provisions had feet I would have no trouble. But it is completely helpless and must be carried. So perhaps you would permit your horse to carry the bundle to Nicoya for me, while I walk behind."

Again the horseman shook his head.

"I couldn't possibly burden my horse with such a bundle," the horseman said. And he rode away in the direction of Nicoya.

The Indian watched him go. When the horse and rider were out of sight, he said to himself, "If I must walk, I will eat and gain strength." So he opened his bag and brought out some of the food, which he began to eat. He took out a bottle of wine to quench his thirst. Leisurely and contentedly he ate and drank.

Meanwhile, the rich, proud rider was thinking about the Indian who had asked for help. "Whatever would my friends have said if they had seen me carrying an Indian's pack?" he thought. He could not get his mind off the bundle. He remembered that he had seen plantains and mangos through the holes in the bag. He seemed to recall seeing the neck of a bottle poking out.

The sun beat down on him, and gradually he realized that he was hungry and thirsty, and that Nicoya was still a long way off. Suddenly he stopped his horse, saying to himself, "I was a fool. The peasant's bag was full of food and drink. Undoubtedly he would have shared some of it with me."

He turned his horse around and rode back to the place where he had left the Indian. He arrived in time to see the man repacking his bundle. On the ground under the tree were the remains of the Indian's meal.

"Look here," the horseman said, "I have been thinking it over and I've decided to help you with your bundle. Put it up here on the horse."

The Indian smiled. "Thank you, Señor," he said. "You are kind. But everything is different now. I have eaten, and I feel much stronger. Also, my bag of provisions is much lighter. So I am able to finish the journey to Nicoya without inconveniencing you."

He slung the bundle over his shoulder and took to the road.

As for the proud horseman, there was nothing for him to do but go on riding, thinking of the good meal he had missed because he had refused to perform a generous act when he could have.

THE ORIGIN OF THE BALSAM TREE
[El Salvador]

Long ago, it is said, an Indian youth named Hoitzi loved a girl named Nabá. Hoitzi was the son of a chieftain, and Nabá was the daughter of a chieftain, but they were of different tribes and her father refused to give his consent to their marriage. The girl's father, Atlcatl, hated Hoitzi because he was of the Maya-Quichi people, and he sought by every means to keep the young man and his daughter apart.

At last, in despair, Hoitzi resolved to come with his warriors and take Nabá away. He waited for a time when he might catch Atlcatl by surprise. And one dark, stormy night he came. The rain was falling, the rivers had become raging torrents, and the waves broke against the rocky seashore with a sound like thunder. Hoitzi and his warriors approached the town, sure that they would not be seen.

But, alas, Atlcatl's men were ready. They lay in wait for Hoitzi and his warriors, and they caught them in an ambush outside the town. A terrible battle took place. Hoitzi's men were outnumbered, and finally they were overcome. Those who could escape did so, leaving behind on the battlefield their dead and wounded comrades. Among the dead was Hoitzi himself.

Nabá heard the news of the battle. She went out secretly to the battlefield with six of her most devoted attendants, while Atlcatl and his warriors celebrated their victory.

Guided by the cries and groans of the wounded, the seven women found their way through the storm. There Nabá and her companions spent the entire night comforting the wounded, bandaging their broken limbs, and bringing them water to quench their thirst.

Then, as the morning sun rose, Atlcatl was told by one of his guards that seven women were on the battlefield comforting the enemy wounded. Atlcatl came to the scene in anger. And when he saw his daughter Nabá kneeling on the sodden earth by the dead Hoitzi, his head in her lap, Atlcatl's rage was uncontrollable. He seized a bow from one of his warriors and shot Nabá through the heart. On Atlcatl's orders, the six other women were also slain. Nabá and her six companions were buried there where they died.

The people of the town avoided the site of the battle for many years, because of the tragic things that had happened there. But later, when they came again, they found that where Nabá and her friends had been buried there had grown seven beautiful trees. These trees, of a kind that had never been seen before, gave off a strong perfume, and the dark sap which flowed from their bark was found to heal wounds in a miraculous way. Thus, from the compassion and mercy of Nabá and her friends there had sprung up Balsam trees, known among Atlcatl's people as Nabá trees.

In time these trees multiplied and spread, and a day came when the Pacific shores of this region came to be known as the Balsam Coast. Today the Balsam tree gives up its precious sap to heal friend and foe alike. And, like the sandalwood tree in other parts of the world, "it perfumes the ax which lays it low."

THE FALL OF THE EARTH GIANTS
[Honduras—An Ancient Mayan Myth]

When the earth was created, the Maya Indians believed, it happened this way: The God Hurakan, in the form of a mighty wind, rose and swept over the entire universe, which was still in darkness. Hurakan cried out "Earth!" And solid land appeared for the first time. Then the chief gods met to discuss what should be done next. They created animals. After that they decided to make people. They carved the first people out of wood, but these newly made creatures showed little reverence to the gods. So the gods became angry and determined to destroy them. They caused a mighty flood to come over the earth, and thus the first people were destroyed. A few of the first people escaped, however, and their descendants are still to be found in the woods in the form of monkeys. Later the gods created a new race of men who now people the earth.

But there remained after the flood other creatures who angered the gods. One was the giant Vukub-Cakix, whose name meant seven-times-the-color-of-fire. He was so named because of his brilliant color. His teeth were of emerald, and his body shone like polished silver and gold. Vukub-Cakix, the earth giant, boasted of his great power and refused to recognize the gods as his superiors. So they sent two warrior-gods to destroy him and his race. These heavenly warriors were twins. The first was named Hun-

243

Apu, meaning chief. The second was named Xbalanque, meaning little tiger.

They sought out Vukub-Cakix's great fruit tree, where the giant ate his breakfast every day. They climbed it, eating the golden fruit that it bore. Then Vukub-Cakix came and went up into the tree to eat, but he saw that the fruit had been picked, and he saw the two warriors there. The earth giant leaped forward to attack them, but Hun-Apu raised a blowpipe to his mouth and shot a poisoned dart at him. The dart struck Vukub-Cakix in the jaw, and he fell to the ground. Hun-Apu went down and grappled with him, but in terrible anger the giant seized Hun-Apu's arm and tore it off. The giant then returned to his house, roaring with the pain of the poisoned dart in his jaw. So full of hate was he for the warrior-gods that he took Hun-Apu's arm and hung it over the fire to roast. Vukub-Cakix tended the arm, turning it so that it would cook evenly. Thus did the giant demonstrate his contempt for the gods.

But Hun-Apu and Xbalanque were not through with Vukub-Cakix. They were determined to finish what they had begun, and to get back Hun-Apu's arm. They went to two powerful magicians for help, and together the four of them approached Vukub-Cakix's house. The magicians disguised themselves as doctors, and the warriors disguised themselves as their sons. While still far off they could hear Vukub-Cakix groaning and heaping insults on the gods. When they arrived they told the giant they had heard his cries of distress and had come to help.

"The demons who shot a poisoned dart into my jaw are responsible," Vukub-Cakix said. "Can you cure the pain?"

"Yes, we can cure it," the magicians said. "We must remove your teeth, but we will replace them with grains of maize."

They quickly removed the teeth, and they put grains of white maize where the teeth had been. But when they had done this, Vukub-Cakix's strength ebbed, his gold and silver color faded away, and he sank into unconsciousness and died.

Then Hun-Apu went forward and took his arm from over the fire, and the magicians replaced it on his body, and it was as good as before.

But Vukub-Cakix's two sons remained to be dealt with. One was Zipacna, the heaper-of-mountains, who piled one mountain on another. The second was Cabrakan, the tearer-down-of-mountains.

First, Hun-Apu and Xbalanque sought out the region where Zipacna lived. There they gathered together four hundred men, and instructed them how to bring about Zipacna's death. When the men had heard the instructions of the warrior-gods, they prepared to build a great house. They excavated for the foundations, and then they cut down a large tree for one of the timbers. After a while they heard Zipacna crashing through the forest. When he came to where they were waiting, he looked at them and laughed. He said, "Oh little ones, can't you carry this tree now that you've cut it down?"

They answered, "No, even four hundred of us cannot lift it."

Zipacna, the heaper-of-mountains, picked the tree up and put it on his shoulder and carried it to the site of the building.

The men asked him to take it down into the deep ditch they had excavated. Zipacna went down with his load, but before he could come out the men began to hurl great timbers and stones down on him. Zipacna moved quickly into a side tunnel, prepared for a cellar. The four hundred men filled the ditch, and imagining the giant to be dead, they began to dance. From where he sat below, Zipacna heard their celebration. He fed their glee by giving several strands of his hair to the ants, who carried them to the surface. When the men saw the hairs from Zipacna's head, they were doubly sure of his death. They built their great house over the tree trunks and stones which they imagined covered Zipacna's corpse. And when it was finished, they entered to celebrate their victory. They brought out much *pulque* and drank heavily and became drunk.

Under the earth Zipacna listened, waiting for his revenge. Suddenly, arising in all his giant might, he burst through the ground and cast the house and all its occupants into the air. The men were hurled with such force into the sky that they remained there and became stars, forming the constellation that we call the Pleiades.

Thus Hun-Apu and Xbalanque had failed. But they resolved that Zipacna must not escape. They contrived another plan. First they fashioned a huge crab out of wood, painting it in its natural colors so that it seemed alive. They placed their crab in a cave at the bottom of a ravine, and they undermined the mountain above so that it was ready to fall. Disguising themselves as fishermen, they went to the river where Zipacna was fishing. When Zipacna appeared, they said, "We have just seen a giant crab in the cave at the bottom of the ravine. It is big, and we are afraid, otherwise we would have caught it."

When Zipacna heard this he laughed and went at once to the cave entrance. He saw the great crab inside, and he entered. Then Hun-Apu and Xbalanque caused the mountain to collapse over his head. The earth slid down and boulders thundered down into the ravine, sealing the entrance to the cave. The landslide filled the ravine and covered the cave to a great depth, and a cloud of red dust hung in the air. Zipacna the earth giant, the heaper-of-mountains, made mighty efforts to free himself. The mountain heaved and shook as he struggled. Hun-Apu and Xbalanque, fearful that he might escape again, wrought powerful magic and turned Zipacna into stone.

So now Vukub-Cakix and Zipacna were accounted for. There was still one more earth giant, Cabrakan, the second son of Vukub-Cakix. He was the most proud and boastful of all, the tearer-down-of-mountains. When the warrior-gods found him, Cabrakan was busy throwing mountains around. One by one he seized the mountains, wrenched them loose from where they stood, and hurled them into the air. So proud was Cabrakan of his strength that he chose only the large mountains for his sport. Of the small mountains he took no notice whatsoever.

When he saw Hun-Apu and Xbalanque he stopped his play and asked, "What are your names?"

"We have no names," they said. "We are hunters who roam through the mountains looking for game to shoot. As we never meet anyone in this wilderness, we need no names."

Cabrakan looked at them disdainfully.

They said to him, "We have heard of you. We would like to see you demonstrate your great strength."

This aroused Cabrakan's pride and boastfulness. He replied, "I will show you. Choose a mountain for me to move. I shall smash it into little pieces."

"First you must eat," Hun-Apu said. "Aren't you hungry after a whole morning of such work?"

"Let us eat, then," Cabrakan said. "Where is the food?"

The warrior-gods looked overhead. A large bird was flying in the sky at a great height. They raised their blowpipes to their mouths and shot darts into the air. Both darts found their mark at the same instant, and the bird fell to the earth. Cabrakan was surprised at the marksmanship of the hunters. Hun-Apu and Xbalanque made a fire. They smeared a coating of mud over the outside of the bird, as was their way of cooking, and they put it into the coals. But what Cabrakan did not know was that the mud had been made from poisonous earth called *tizate*. As the bird cooked, the poison from the earth seeped into the meat. When they took the bird from the fire, they removed the baked mud and the feathers. They gave the food to Cabrakan, who ate it greedily. When he was finished, he said, "Now I will tear down a mountain for you."

"The mountain we choose is that tall peak in the east," Hun-Apu said. "We will see now whether you are simply a boaster."

But already the poison was at work, and Cabrakan began to feel strange pains.

"Where is it?" Cabrakan asked. "Somehow I don't seem to see it clearly."

"There," Xbalanque said, "the tall peak in the east where the sun rises."

They walked awhile, and Cabrakan said, "My eyes are dim today. Somehow I don't see the mountain you speak of."

"Perhaps you are afraid to see it," Hun-Apu said. "Perhaps you are not a mountain mover but only a boaster."

Cabrakan became angry. He said, "I am no boaster! Lead me to the mountain and I will demolish it!"

Hun-Apu took him by the hand and led him. At last they were at the base of the tall peak. "This is the mountain," Hun-Apu said. "Can you see it now?"

"No, I can't see it," Cabrakan said, his eyes peering sightlessly at the wall of rock in front of him. His knees began to shake. They knocked together and made a sound like war drums. The sweat poured from his forehead and ran in a stream down the hillside.

"Are you going to throw the mountain or not?" Hun-Apu asked derisively.

"He cannot do it," Xbalanque said. "He is only an idle boaster."

Cabrakan heard only faintly. He reached forward and took hold of the mountain in a mighty effort. But it was too late. The poison from the *tizate* rushed through his blood, and with a groan he fell and died.

Thus perished the last of the earth giants, whom Hun-Apu and Xbalanque had been sent to destroy.

THE EMERALD LIZARD

[Guatemala]

This is a tale about the good Brother Pedro San Joseph de Bethancourt, who lived three centuries ago in the City of Santiago de Guatemala. It is said that this saintly man was walking one morning on the outskirts of the city, deep in thought. For himself, Brother Pedro had no problems. He wore simple and shabby clothes, and sought nothing else. His concerns were for the poor and sick, and he had established a place on the edge of the city where they could be cared for. Every day nuns brought baskets of bread to the place to help feed the hungry, yet there was far from enough to go around. There were more poor than bread, more sick than beds, and Brother Pedro was pondering how more help could be given to those who suffered.

As he turned these problems over in his mind, he saw a poor Indian approaching along the road. Leaning wearily on his staff, the Indian came slowly to where Brother Pedro was and greeted him sadly and sorrowfully.

"What troubles you, my son?" Brother Pedro asked, seeing the man's distress.

"Oh, Padre," the Indian said, "I am in great trouble. My name is Juan Manuel Jurakan. My wife is sick, she is dying, and I have no money for medicine. My little boys too are dying of hunger, and I have nothing for them to eat. I swear to you that it is the truth, just as I have told it."

Brother Pedro looked at the suffering man's face, and he knew it was the truth. The bread brought by the nuns that day was already gone, and as for money, there was none. Brother Pedro absent-mindedly reached into his pockets, feeling for a stray coin which might lie there forgotten. But his pockets were empty, as they usually were. Not a single tiny coin did he find.

He turned his eyes upward toward the sky, seeking an answer to this problem. Surely, he thought, on this beautiful day there must be some way of softening the misery of the man who stood there before him!

As they stood together at the edge of the road, there was a sound at their feet, and, from under a clump of blue flowers, a small green lizard scurried out into the sunlight. With a tender smile, Brother Pedro reached down and caught the little lizard and gently placed it in the hands of Juan Manuel Jurakan.

The man looked into Brother Pedro's face in wonder. Then he looked at the lizard he had received, and great was his astonishment to see that it was now motionless and lifeless. Still it was green, but it was the green color of emeralds. And suddenly he saw that the little lizard had truly turned into emerald, and that Brother Pedro had wrought a miracle.

Juan Manuel Jurakan gave tearful thanks to Brother Pedro, and he took his emerald lizard to a merchant in the market place to exchange it for money for food and medicine.

The years passed. Juan Manuel's sons grew up and became traders in blankets and shawls. Juan Manuel himself now had many cattle and much land, yet he lived simply and saved his money, coin by coin, so that he could buy back the emerald lizard which had changed his fortunes. A day came when he went to the merchant in the market and bought back the emerald lizard, and then he set out in search of Brother Pedro.

When at last he found Brother Pedro, he was greatly surprised. Brother Pedro was now old and gray, and his clothes were as ragged and worn as they used to be.

The Indian greeted him, saying, "Greetings to you, Padre. Don't you remember me? I am Juan Manuel Jurakan. I am the one to whom you gave the emerald lizard many years ago, and now I have brought it back."

Brother Pedro searched in his mind, trying to remember the incident.

"Take it, Padre," Juan Manuel said. "It brought me much good fortune. Take it, and rest from your labors now. It is valuable and will make life easy for you."

He opened the cloth in which the emerald lizard was wrapped, and he took the jeweled object and held it up for Brother Pedro to see.

Smiling now, Brother Pedro remembered and received it. Gently he set it down on the earth, and instantly it turned again into a live green lizard, which scurried off and disappeared in the tall grass.

SEÑOR COYOTE AND THE DOGS
[*Mexico*]

This is a story of Señor Coyote, the trickster and the numskull. Of this creature the other animals truly say that his cleverness is equaled only by his stupidity.

One day when Señor Coyote was walking along the level valley between two mountains, two large dogs that had been trying for a long time to catch him sprang from behind a large stone. The coyote tried to run to the woods, but the dogs had seen to it that he would have to take to the open country. As he ran around the bushes and jumped across rocks and across dry arroyos, making the dust fly, he thought that he was getting away from the dogs behind. Their yelps of *yo! yo! yo!* were getting a little fainter, he thought. Gasping for breath, he looked around for the best direction to take.

But while he was trying to make up his mind, two other dogs rose up out of nowhere and made up his mind for him. He was forced to turn back in the direction from which he had come. The dogs had planned to take turns racing the coyote back and forth across the desert until he was too tired to go any further. The dogs behind him were coming closer, and the coyote knew he was running toward the other two, who were waiting. He knew that he would have to act fast.

Upon the side of the mountain he saw something dark

and round that made him take heart. He wished that it were closer. It was a cave. And now he saw two dogs in front of him and heard two dogs behind. He made a sharp turn and raced for the foot of the mountain. Now all four dogs were behind him, but they were running faster and coming closer. They were so close that Señor Coyote could hear them argue about which one would get him. He saw the cave in front of him and a chill of fear went through his body as the thought came to him that maybe the cave opening was big enough for the dogs to enter after him. But the dogs were so close now that they were snapping hairs out of the end of Señor Coyote's tail. And so with a flying dive, he landed inside the mouth of the cave.

Señor Coyote was lucky. The hole was too small for the dogs. Inside the cave he ran as far back as he could. Outside, the dogs complained and whined and pawed around the cave awhile and then were heard no more.

This was easily the worst fright the coyote ever had. But once safe inside the cave, he began to feel brave again. He began to think he was quite a fellow to be able to get rid of the dogs. As his weary limbs became rested, a desire to boast and brag stole over him. There was no one in the cave to talk to, so he began chatting with the various parts of his body which had had some part in the race against the dogs.

"*Patos*," he said, looking at his four feet one at a time, "what did you do?"

"We carried you away," said the feet. "We kicked up dust to blind the bad dogs. We jumped the rocks and bushes and brought you here."

"*Bueno, bueno,*" the coyote said, "good, good!   You feet did very well."   Then he spoke to his ears.

"Ears, what did you do?"

"We listened to the right and the left.   We listened to know how far behind the dogs were, so that feet would know how fast to run."

"Splendid!" said the coyote.   "And eyes, what did you do?"

"We pointed out the road through the rocks and brush and canyons.   We were on the lookout for your safety. We saw this cave."

"Marvelous!" said the coyote with a great laugh.   "What a great fellow I am to have such fine eyes, feet, and ears." And so overcome was Señor Coyote with his own self and the great things he had done in his life that he reached over to pat himself on the back.   And it was then that he saw his tail back there.

"Aha, my tail," he said, "I had almost forgotten about you.   Come, tell me what you did in this battle with the dogs."

The tail could tell by the tone of the coyote's voice that he did not think too highly of him and so did not answer.

"About all you did was add extra load," said the coyote. "More than anything else, you held me back.   Almost got me caught, too.   You let the dogs grab the end of you. But let's hear from you.   Speak up!"

"What did I do?" asked the tail.   "I motioned to the dogs, like this, telling them to come on and get you.   While you were running I was back there urging the dogs to come on. Through the dust they could see me in my whiteness waving."

Señor Coyote's scowl was becoming darker and darker.

"*Silencio!*" he shouted, stuttering and stammering with anger. "What do you mean?" And he reached back and gave a slap at his tail, and then reached around and bit at it.

"You do not belong here in this cave with the rest of us, you traitor!" And the coyote was backing his tail toward the door of the cave. "Out you go," he said. "Outside! There is no room in here for you. You belong outside. You are on the side of the dogs. You tried to help them catch me, and then you brag about it! Outside!"

And the coyote pointed to his tail with one hand, and to the round piece of daylight, which was the cave door, he pointed with the other hand. "Get out!"

And the coyote backed his tail out the door into the open air. The dogs, who had been listening to the talk inside, were waiting hidden outside. When the coyote's tail appeared through the cave door, the dogs grabbed it. And of course Señor Coyote was jerked out of the cave by his tail. And what the dogs did to him is another story.

THE BEEF TONGUE OF ORULA
[*Cuba*]

The great god Obatalá had as his helper another god by the name of Orula. When Obatalá determined one day to appoint a ruler of the world, he thought first of Orula. But he was hesitant and undecided, for he feared that perhaps Orula was too young and inexperienced for such a task. And so Obatalá decided to test Orula's wisdom. He sent for Orula and asked him to prepare the finest possible meal.

Orula went off to the public market and looked at everything that was for sale. At last he bought a beef tongue and brought it home. He cooked it with great care, preparing it with all kinds of herbs and spices. When it was done, he carried it to Obatalá, and Obatalá tasted it. Never had Obatalá eaten anything so good. When the food was gone, he complimented Orula and said to him, "Tell me, Orula, when you had the choice of all the different meats in the market, why did you choose a tongue?"

"Great Obatalá," Orula replied, "the tongue is a very significant thing. With a tongue you can praise good works and compliment those who do good deeds. You can tell good news and influence people in the way they should go. You can even promote people to high rank," he added, smiling at Obatalá.

"All you have said is very true," Obatalá replied, thinking to himself: "Orula is indeed filled with knowledge."

But Obatalá decided to test Orula further, and he said to him: "You have prepared for me the best of all dishes. Now I want you to prepare for me the worst food you can imagine."

So once again Orula went to the market. After looking at everything there, he again bought a beef tongue. He brought it home and prepared it with spices and herbs, and when it was cooked he carried it to Obatalá and put it before him.

Obatalá was astonished. He said, "First you brought me this dish and represented it as the best of good things. Now you again bring tongue and represent it as the worst of bad things. How can you explain this?"

Orula replied, "Great Obatalá, the tongue is a very significant thing. With a tongue you can belittle a man's endeavors and destroy his good reputation. You can influence people to their disadvantage, and with an evil word you can deprive them of their livelihood. With a tongue you can betray a country and sell its people into slavery."

When Obatalá heard this, he said, "All that you have said is true. You are wise beyond your years."

And then and there he made Orula master of the world.

UNCLE BOUKI RENTS A HORSE
[Haiti]

Somewhere in the Haitian mountains were two men called Uncle Bouki and Ti Malice. Bouki was large, strong, and slow. He had a reputation for wanting to get ahead in life. But somehow he had a knack for getting into trouble. As for Ti Malice, his name meant "mischief." He was small, lazy, and sharp-witted. He had a reputation for getting along in life the easy way—tricking other people. Most people avoided him, but Bouki admired Ti Malice's talent for trickery. As a result, he was always in difficulty. There was that time that Uncle Bouki wanted to rent a horse to take his crops down to the city.

It all started when he went to his friend Moussa to borrow his burro. "Bouki," Moussa said, "my burro ran off yesterday and we haven't been able to find her. We've looked as far as the top of the hill, and there isn't even a track."

"Woy!" Bouki said. "What about my yams? How am I going to get them to market?"

"Why don't you borrow a horse from Mr. Toussaint?" Moussa suggested.

"Toussaint! That stingy old man! He'll charge me rent. He'll charge me for even talking to him!"

Bouki frowned and sulked and pushed out his lips, but finally he went to Toussaint's place to rent a horse.

"It will cost you fifteen gourds," Toussaint said. "And

you'd better take care of him! Don't try to make him carry as much as you put on your own head, either. This is a good horse."

"I only have five gourds now," Bouki said.

"I'll take it," Toussaint said, snatching the money. "You can give me ten more tomorrow when you come for the horse."

All the way home Bouki mumbled and grumbled. But he had to have a horse, that was all there was to it.

In the morning when he got up to prepare for market, he stuck his head out the door and saw Moussa riding toward the house on his burro.

"Here is the burro, Bouki!" Moussa called out. "She came home in the middle of the night. I heard her rolling in the coffee plants to scratch her back."

"Wah!" Bouki wailed. "I already rented a horse from Mr. Toussaint!"

"Take him back and use mine," Moussa said.

"I don't have him yet," Bouki said, "but I already gave Toussaint five gourds! He'll never give it back! He sticks to money like a fly to fresh meat!"

While Bouki was carrying on, Ti Malice came along the trail and stopped by the gate to listen. "Take me along," he said to Bouki. "I'll get your money back from Toussaint."

Bouki's face broke into happy little wrinkles. "What a wonderful idea!" he said. "You could get money out of a coconut!"

So Uncle Bouki and Ti Malice went together to Toussaint's house.

"We've come for the horse," Malice said to Toussaint. "And he'd better be fed, too."

"There he is under the mango tree," Toussaint said. "But first give me the ten gourds."

"Just a minute," Malice said. "We have to see if he's big enough."

"He's big enough. A horse is a horse," Toussaint said. "Don't try to back out of this deal. Uncle Bouki rented him for fifteen gourds, and that's that."

"Just a minute," Ti Malice said. "We have to measure him." He took a measuring tape out of his pocket and started to measure the horse's back.

"Let's see now," he said to Uncle Bouki. "You'll need about eighteen inches, and you can sit here in the middle. Then I'll need about fifteen inches, and I'll sit here. Madame Malice can sit behind me, and she'll need about eighteen inches. Madame Bouki can sit in the front, and she'll have to have about twenty inches. . . ."

"What's going on?" Toussaint said. "You can't put four people on that horse!"

"Don't bother us," Ti Malice said, still measuring with his tape. "We have to figure where the children will sit. Jean Bouki can go here on the horse's neck, Boukino can sit in his lap, and we can strap Boukinette right here if we're careful. . . ."

"Listen!" Toussaint said, the perspiration starting to run down his face. "You must be crazy! A horse can't carry so many people!"

"He can try," Ti Malice said. "At least, that's *his* end of the job. *Our* problem is to figure how to get the whole

261

party on him for the trip to Saut d'Eau for the festivities."

"You're not going to ride him all the way to Saut d'Eau!" Toussaint moaned. "He'll wear his feet off right down to the knees!"

"We can put my children here," Malice said, measuring behind the horse's ears. "But they'll have to push together pretty tight."

"You're absolutely crazy!" Toussaint said. "You can't have the horse at all!"

"A bargain's a bargain," Malice said. "You rented him to us and now we're going to use him. Uncle Bouki, where will I put the baby?"

"Baby?" Uncle Bouki said. He closed his mouth and licked his dry lips. He just looked at Malice in bewilderment.

"Here, we'll put the baby here!" Malice said. "As for the two pigs and the goats, we can put them in the saddlebags. . . ."

Toussaint wiped the perspiration from his bald head. "Pigs and goats!" he said. "Are you trying to kill the horse? The deal is off! This animal isn't a steamship!"

"A bargain's a bargain," Malice said firmly. "We'll take the matter to court." Bouki nodded his head vigorously in agreement.

"Here!" Toussaint said. "Here's your five gourds back!"

"You rented him out for fifteen, and now you give five back?" Malice said. "What do you take us for?"

"Yes, what for?" Bouki echoed.

"All Bouki gave me was five," Toussaint said.

"You admit you rented him for fifteen, don't you?" Malice said. "If you don't give fifteen back, we'll take you to court for not keeping your contract."

"Where'll we put grandmother?" Bouki asked suddenly, looking at the horse.

"Here!" Toussaint panted, shoving fifteen gourds into Malice's hands. "And get away from that horse!" He jumped on its back and rode away at a wild gallop.

Bouki and Malice began to laugh. They laughed until their stomachs hurt and tears ran down their faces. They snorted and choked and gasped for breath thinking about Toussaint. Finally, when they were too weak to laugh any more they walked down the hill to Bouki's house. Madame Bouki served them coffee, and all the while they were drinking it they were snorting and sputtering.

"Wah!" Bouki wailed. "I've never seen anything so funny in my life!"

"Wye! It was a scream!" Malice said. He put on his hat and went down the trail toward the city.

"This is certainly a day I'll remember!" Bouki said. "I gave him *five*, and he gave *fifteen* back! The stingiest man in Haiti!"

He put his hand in his pocket. Slowly the happy look went out of his face. He tried another pocket. He began to scowl.

"What's the matter?" Madame Bouki said.

Bouki said "Wah" again faintly. He kept going through his pockets with his hands. Then suddenly he let out a roar. "Wye! Where's that thief Malice! He didn't give me the fifteen gourds!"

He bounded to the trail and looked up and down, but

there was no sign of Malice. Bouki's roaring died down into a feeble whimper. He came back to the house and sat down.

"Yes, it's certainly a day to remember," Madame Bouki said.

Uncle Bouki was silent a long time. "I don't think we could have done it," he said at last.

"Done what?" Madame Bouki asked.

"Put grandmother on the horse," Bouki said.

THE KING'S TOWER
[*Dominican Republic*]

Long ago there lived a King who got it into his head that he wanted to touch the moon. He thought and thought about ways in which this might be accomplished. Instead of attending to affairs of government during his waking hours, he thought up plans which would help him achieve his fantastic ambition. At night he often lay awake trying to solve the problem of how to touch the moon, and when he slept he dreamed about it.

He determined at last that some sort of tower would have to be built, and so he called upon an unfortunate carpenter and commanded him to build a structure which would reach the sky. The poor man was quite aware of the impossibility of the project, and, although he wandered about busily with his tools and his helpers, he built nothing at all. A number of weeks passed, and the King became impatient and irritable. He sent for the carpenter and told him he would have three more days to construct the tower. If he failed to do it, the King said, he would be executed.

So the carpenter wandered around some more with his hammer in his hand, not knowing what to do. One day passed. Then two. And on the third day an idea came into the desperate man's head, and he went to see the King.

"I have studied the matter from every angle," he told the King, "and I now see how it can be done. But when the tower is constructed, I think it would be better for me to make the ascent."

"Certainly not!" the King replied indignantly. "It is I who shall make the ascent! Whoever heard of a carpenter rising to such heights?"

So the carpenter then told the King his plan, and the King ordered everyone in the city to bring boxes and crates to the palace grounds. Under the carpenter's direction, the crates and boxes were piled one on the other, and at last there wasn't a single box or crate left. So the King ordered trees to be chopped down, and the trees were sawed up into planks and more boxes were made. In this way, every large tree in the city was felled, and every box that was made was piled on the tower. Then the King began to climb. He climbed to the very top and stretched out his hand to touch the moon. It seemed that he needed only a few more inches, and he called to the people below to bring one more box. But there wasn't a box to be had, nor was there any wood with which to make a box.

The King was angry. He was determined not to fail in achieving his greatest ambition. And at last he had a brilliant idea. He called out to the carpenters and ordered them to take the box from the bottom, the one on which the others were piled, and bring it to the top. The carpenters looked at one another in consternation. But the King's words were law, and they were loyal subjects. So when the King shouted his commands a second time, they

266

hesitated no longer and pulled out the bottom box as he had ordered.

What happened then is easy enough to imagine. Not one hair of the head of that King has ever been found, even to this day.

PAUL BUNYAN'S CORNSTALK
[*United States of America*]

Paul Bunyan was the fellow who invented the ax with two edges so a man could stand between two trees and chop them both down at the same time. As it turned out, Paul was the only man who could do that trick, but the other lumberjacks used the double-bitted ax anyway, because they didn't have to sharpen the blades so often. Paul Bunyan also had other tricks. Most lumberjacks used to cut off the tops of the pines before they felled them. But when Paul was in a hurry, he'd wait till a tree started falling; then he'd get set with his ax and lop off the top of the tree as it came down.

Nothing Paul Bunyan ever did was small. He had an ox named Babe, who used to help him with his logging work. Babe was just about the most phenomenal ox in Michigan. His color was blue, and he stood ninety hands high. If you happened to hang on the tip of one horn, it's doubtful if you could have seen the tip of the other, even on a clear day. One day when Paul had Babe out plowing, the ox was stung by a Michigan deer fly about the size of a bushel basket. Babe took off across the country dragging the plow behind him, right across Indiana, Illinois, and Missouri, with the deer fly bringing up the rear. After a while Babe veered south and didn't stop till he got to the Rio Grande. The plow that Babe was hitched to dug a furrow four miles wide and two hundred miles long.   You can check it in your own geography book.   They call it Grand Canyon nowadays.

Even the storms that Paul was in were big.   The biggest of all was the one they call the Big Blue Snow.   It snowed for two months straight, and the way the drifts piled up only the tops of the tallest pines were showing.   Lumber-jacks went out that winter on their snowshoes and cut off all the pine tops.   It saved them a lot of time when spring came around.   Babe the blue ox didn't get a wink of sleep, though, from December till the first of March.   It seems that standing out there in the weather the way he was, the snow that fell on his back melted and ran down his tail, and once it got there it froze into ice.   Babe's tail kept getting heavier and heavier, and it drew on his hide so hard it just pulled his eyelids wide open and kept them that way.   Babe never did get his eyes closed until the spring thaw came and melted the ice off his tail.

But the Big Blue Snow wasn't anything compared to the big drouth that started in Saginaw County and spread out as far as the Alleghenies in the East and the Rockies in the West.   It all started with Paul Bunyan's vegetable garden. Paul planted some corn and some pumpkins.   One of those cornstalks was six feet high before the others had sprouted. In two weeks it was tall as a house and growing like crazy. About the time it was as big as a fifty-year-old pine, people began to come in from all over the county to see it.   It was growing out of the ground so fast it was pulling up stones that even the frost couldn't heave out.   Same kind of thing, more or less, happened to one of the pumpkin vines.   It grew so fast it just darted around like a Massauga rattlesnake.

It climbed into any place where there was an opening. People had to keep their windows closed. The ones that didn't had to cut their way out of their beds with a brush knife. Sometimes that vine would grow into one window and out another between sunset and sunrise. Things weren't too bad until the vine blossomed and the pumpkins came out. They were about the size of hogsheads—the *little* pumpkins, that is—and when the vine whipped back and forth looking for someplace to grow it just snapped the pumpkins around like crab apples on a string. People had to be mighty alert to keep from getting hit by those pumpkins. One man lost a team of horses that way, and half a dozen good barns and one silo were stoved in.

But the real problem started when the corn and pumpkin roots began to soak up all the water out of the ground. Farms for sixty miles around went dry—fields, springs, and wells. The pine woods turned yellow from lack of moisture. The Au Sable River just turned into a trickle, and pretty soon there wasn't anything there but dry mud. The next thing that happened was that the water in the Great Lakes began to go down. It went down so fast in Lake Huron it left the fish hanging in the air. When things began to look real bad, folks came and told Paul Bunyan he'd just have to get rid of his corn and pumpkins. Paul was reasonable about it. First he went after the pumpkin vine. He spent four hours racing around trying to catch hold of the end, and finally did it by trapping it in a barn. He hitched Babe up to the end of the vine, but as fast as Babe pulled the vine grew. Babe ran faster and faster, and he was near Lake Ontario before he had the vine tight enough to pull it out.

Then Paul sized up his cornstalk. He figured he'd have to chop it down. He sharpened up his ax and spit on his hands. He made a good deep cut in that stalk, but before he could chip out a wedge the stalk grew up six feet, cut and all. Every time he made a cut it would shoot up out of reach before he could swing his ax again. Pretty soon he saw there wasn't any use going on this way. "Only way to kill this stalk is to cut off the top," he said. He hung his ax in his belt and started climbing. In about two hours he was completely out of sight. People just stood around and waited. They stood around two and a half days without any sight of Paul. Lars Larson called, "Paul!" but there was no answer. Erik Erikson and Hans Hanson called, "Paul!" But there wasn't any word from Paul Bunyan. So they waited some more. Two more days went by. No word from Paul. They decided that if everyone yelled at once maybe the sound would carry. So all together the two thousand eight hundred men and boys hollered, "Paul!" And sure enough, they heard his faint voice from up above.

"When you going to top that cornstalk?" they yelled back at him.

"Hasn't that top come down yet?" Paul hollered back. "I cut it off three days ago!"

And it was the truth, too. The stalk stopped growing, the water in the Great Lakes stopped falling, the Au Sable River began to run, the springs began to flow again, and things came back to normal. But it was a narrow escape.

JEAN LABADIE'S DOG
[*Canada*]

Jean Labadie stood in the chicken yard and counted chickens. "If the weasels aren't getting my chickens," Jean Labadie said, "you can bet your life my good neighbor André Drouillard is getting them."

Jean Labadie decided he would catch André Drouillard in the act of absconding with his poultry. So for three nights he slept in the chicken yard with his shotgun by his side. But nothing happened. André's sixth sense must have warned him. Jean Labadie got tired of sleeping with the chickens, and he went back to sleeping in the house. But he was determined to do something about the chicken stealing. The only thing was, he didn't know what. You can't just ask a man if he's stealing your chickens, even if he is. Therefore, Jean Labadie didn't do anything for a while.

Then one day he was helping André Drouillard clear the brush along the fences. While he was working, he found a pile of chicken feathers. Jean Labadie looked at them closely, thinking that they looked mighty like the feathers his own chickens had worn before they'd disappeared. Still and all, you couldn't tell a man, "These look like my chickens' feathers." So Jean Labadie didn't say anything about them. He just kept cutting brush and thinking. "If André thought I had a dog," Jean Labadie said to himself,

"maybe he'd keep away from my chicken yard."   So right
then and there, Jean Labadie made up a big lie.   He invented a dog.   He said to André:

"Have you seen my big black dog yet?"

"Dog?" André said.   "You don't have any dog."

"I didn't used to have a dog," Jean Labadie said, "but
now I do.   I just bought him from the Indians.   Somebody's been stealing my chickens, so I went out and got myself a dog.   He's big and black and mighty mean, and I
don't think anyone will do any more prowling around my
chicken yard."

"Well, well, so you've got a dog now," André remarked.

Jean Labadie looked up.

"See, there he goes now, black as coal, with his big red
tongue hanging out."

André looked.   "I don't see any dog," he said.

"What do you mean you don't see any dog?" Jean Labadie said.   "There he goes right across that ridge."

"Where?" André asked.

"Look, man, look.   Don't you see him lifting those big
black paws one after another?"

"Yes, yes, I see him now!" André said, straining his eyes
for a sight of the big dog with the hanging red tongue and
the paws going one after another.   "Yes, he looks mighty
mean, slinking along the fence like that."

Jean Labadie said nothing more about the dog he had
just invented.   André Drouillard was a little quiet about
it all, but once in a while he looked up towards the ridge to
catch a glimpse of the animal.

Jean was right about one thing.   There were no more

chickens stolen from his chicken yard. He was pretty pleased with himself.

Then one day he met André on the road.

"I saw your big black dog today," André said. "He was running along the fence, his red tongue hanging out, and his big feet going one after another. I got out of his way pretty fast, you can bet your life."

Jean Labadie was amused, but he was also a little disgusted with André's imagination. If the big black dog was running around the countryside, who was guarding the chicken yard?

André met Jean Labadie again on the road one day and said, "Jean, I saw your big black dog this morning. He was on the other side of town chasing rabbits."

Jean said, "Must be some other dog, André. My big black dog is at home guarding the chicken yard."

"If it wasn't your big black dog whose was it?" André said. "Doesn't your dog have a big red tongue that hangs out? When he runs, doesn't he fan the air with his feet?"

"Well, it sounds like my dog," Jean said, "but just the same he's at home now watching the chicken yard."

"You'd better chain him up," André said. "People in town are complaining about your letting a wild Indian dog like that run loose."

Jean wanted to ask how people found out about his dog, but he decided to keep quiet. If he had a dog, people obviously had to know about it.

A few days later André stopped Jean Labadie again. This time he spoke sharply. "You're going to have to do something about that vicious dog of yours. Today on the road he came at me and snapped at my legs. I had to beat him off with a stick."

Jean Labadie didn't know whether to laugh or call André Drouillard a liar. The big black dog had gotten pretty real by now. Finally he said, "All right, I guess I'll have to chain him up." He put his fingers in his mouth and gave a loud whistle. "Here boy! Here boy!" he called to the dog. André Drouillard looked around nervously and left in a hurry.

For awhile Jean Labadie heard no more about it. Then one day when he was in the store buying roofing nails, Madame Villeneuve came up to him and said, "Jean Labadie, you ought to be ashamed the way you let that fierce dog run loose in town."

"He's a fierce dog, that's true," Jean Labadie replied, "but he's chained up at home."

"Maybe he *was* chained up," Madame Villeneuve said, "but he's not chained up any more. He's running around with his red tongue hanging out, making his big black paws go this way and that way. He even bared his teeth at me this afternoon."

Jean Labadie began to worry. It looked like things were getting out of control with the dog. He thought maybe he ought to get rid of him. So he said to Madame Villeneuve, "I'll tell you what I'll do, Madame Villeneuve. Tomorrow morning I'll take that dog back to the Indians."

"It's about time," Madame Villeneuve said.

The next morning Jean hitched his horse and got in the cart. He waited until he saw André Drouillard, then he whistled loudly and made a great show of getting the dog

275

in with him. As he drove past André's house, André shouted, "Taking him back, Jean?"

"Back where I got him," Jean Labadie replied, and he drove down the road and headed for the Indian village.

He spent the day talking with his Indian friends, and in the late afternoon he headed for home. As he came around the bend near André Drouillard's house, a feeling of foreboding came over him. He saw André waiting at the gate.

"What's the matter?" Jean Labadie asked.

"Plenty's the matter," André said. "Your big black dog's come home. Beat you here by an hour. I was just coming out to milk, and what should I see but the dog coming up the road, his big red tongue hanging out of his mouth."

Jean Labadie exploded. "André Drouillard," he shouted, "you're a liar! I just left that big black dog with the Indians!"

"Oh?" André said coldly. "Now you're calling your neighbors liars?" And he turned and went into the house.

Jean Labadie groaned. After all the pains he'd gone to, he had messed everything up. Now he had called André Drouillard a liar. He might as well have called him a chicken thief in the first place.

The way it turned out, Madame Villeneuve saw the big black dog running behind her house. Henri Dupuis saw him skulking behind the store. Delphine Langlois saw him running through the graveyard. And everyone was angry at Jean Labadie. But Jean figured there was no use taking the dog to the Indian village again, he'd just come back.

A few days later, when Jean Labadie was sitting in front of the blacksmith shop, André Drouillard came riding up at a great pace on his horse. "Where is Dr. Brisson?" André shouted. "Somebody get Dr. Brisson!"

"What's the matter?" everyone called out at once.

André raised a bleeding hand and pointed it at Jean Labadie.

"*His* big black dog bit me!" he said.

Jean sat there with his mouth open. Seeing a dog that isn't there is one thing. Being bitten by such a dog is something else again. He closed his mouth and went over where everyone was looking at André's bleeding hand.

"It doesn't look like a dog bite to me, it looks more like an ax cut," Jean Labadie said.

This made everyone angry. "First he lets his wild Indian dog run loose," they said, "and then when someone gets bitten he says it's an ax cut!"

Jean felt very helpless about the dog. At last he said, "My friends, I think we'll have to put an end to this matter once and for all. I'll give André two chickens for the damage to his hand. And what's more important, I think I'll have to shoot that big black dog."

The crowd was silent. Jean Labadie said, "Follow me." He walked down the road to his house, with the crowd behind. He went in the door and came out a minute later with his gun. "Stand here," Jean Labadie said, "and watch me kill the big black dog."

He went out by the barn and whistled. He whistled again. Then he called out, "Here he comes!"

The crowd moved back toward the fence to get out of the

way. Madame Villeneuve said tensely, "I see him be-hind the barn, with his big red tongue hanging out!" And André Drouillard said, "Also with his big old feet going up and down!"

Jean Labadie raised his gun to his shoulder, aimed care-fully, and fired. "Got him," he said. Delphine Langlois fainted.

"There," Jean Labadie said softly, brushing a tear from his eye, "I've done it. My big black dog is gone for good."

Everyone agreed that Jean Labadie's dog was done for, and they turned and went away. André Drouillard headed for home with two fat chickens under his arm.

As for Jean Labadie, when the people looked over their shoulders they saw him sadly digging a grave for the only dog he ever had.

THE TOROMIRO OF RAPA-NUI

[Chile—A Tale from Easter Island]

In ancient times on the island of Rapa-Nui, which is now called Easter Island, there was a chief by the name of Ariki. Rapa-Nui was a happy and peaceful place—except for one thing. There were sorcerers in the country who cast spells upon the people. These creatures had the power to change their forms, and it was difficult to know who they were because when they went about their business it was in the shape of humans. The people of Rapa-Nui were in a constant state of apprehension. No one knew who the next victim of the sorcerers would be. It came to pass that whenever a stranger was seen on Rapa-Nui, people said to themselves, "Can these be the sorcerers who are tormenting us?" And sometimes when a neighbor appeared to do something a little strange, people thought, "Perhaps this person is the one!" But weeks and months went by, and the identity of the sorcerers was not discovered.

One morning, before the rising of the sun, Chief Ariki, unable to sleep, was walking near the seashore. And suddenly, in the early gray light that comes just before dawn, he saw two figures sleeping on the ground. He came closer to see their faces, and he recognized them as Hitirau and Nuko, two men of the village. He was about to awaken them, to ask why they slept by the edge of the sea, when

279

his eyes turned to their bodies. Ariki's skin tingled with horror. For while the faces were those of ordinary people, the bodies were fleshless, naked skeletons. Ariki knew that he had discovered the sorcerers. He tried to creep away silently, but the sound of his footsteps awoke Hitirau and Nuko. Through the corner of his eye, Ariki saw that when the men awoke their skeletons instantly became covered with flesh, and they were again no different than other people.

Hitirau and Nuko arose and followed the chief. Ariki composed himself and gave no sign that he had discovered their secret. When the two men caught up with him, Nuko said, "Good morning, Ariki, what brings you out to the seashore so early in the morning?"

"I could not sleep. I awakened early, and so I took a walk," Ariki replied.

"And did you see anything unusual this morning?" Hitirau asked him.

"No," Ariki said casually. "I saw nothing unusual. Just what one sees every morning at this hour—the sea, the coral, the sand, and the stars."

Hitirau and Nuko asked no more questions, and Ariki acted as though he knew nothing he hadn't known yesterday or the week before. Yet his mind whirled. He had to let the people of Rapa-Nui know who the sorcerers were. And he knew that if he went to the village and spoke what he had learned, the words would be his last, for the sorcerers would cast a spell on him. He said to himself, "Whatever comes, I must tell the people of Rapa-Nui!" But when he arrived in the village, with Hitirau and Nuko following, his courage failed him. He went into his house and sat thinking. All day he thought, without finding a solution. That night he lay on his mat without sleeping. And at last the answer came to him. He would let the people of Rapa-Nui know about the sorcerers without saying a word.

When day came, Ariki arose and went out in search of a Toromiro tree. He found it, and he had it cut down and brought to his house. He took out his carving tools and began to carve statues out of the Toromiro wood. For seven days he remained in his house. People heard the sound of his chisel and asked each other, "What can Ariki be doing?" But no one could say what Ariki was doing, because no one knew.

On the seventh day Ariki was finished. Before him stood two sets of statues. The first set of statues showed Hitirau and Nuko as the people of Rapa-Nui knew them. So perfect were the portraits that no one could mistake the men whom they represented. The second set of statues portrayed two figures lying down. The faces were the same as in the first set, but the bodies were as Ariki had seen them on the seashore—fleshless skeletons.

Ariki had the statues put up in a public place, where everyone could see them. People came and looked, and they understood. Without saying a word, Ariki had told them the secret of Hitirau and Nuko. With this knowledge, they were able to take precautions against the sorcerers. And their identity being known, Hitirau and Nuko cast no more spells among the people of Rapa-Nui. One day they took their belongings in an outrigger canoe and paddled out to sea. And that was the last that the people of Rapa-Nui saw of them.

The wooden statues made by Ariki can be seen in Easter Island to this day, and they are called Toromiro, after the tree from which they were carved.

NOTES ON THE STORIES

MAUI THE FIRE-BRINGER (*New Zealand*): Ancient Maori legend, based on traditional sources. Maui is one of the great culture heroes of Polynesia, from New Zealand to Hawaii. The details vary from island to island, but in their main lines the myths are common throughout the area, and fragments of the Maui tales are found also in Melanesian lore. In some parts of Polynesia, Maui is credited (in addition to the feats recounted here) with raising the sky to its present position. The Maori, however, believe it was another culture hero, Tane, who performed this act. Among Maui's many accomplishments, according to the Maori, is the capture and imprisonment of the winds, all except the west wind which eluded him. Maui is also thought to be responsible for many kinds of flora and fauna. He kills a giant eel, Tuna, who is molesting his wife; cutting the monster into little pieces, he strews them about, and they become plants and trees and fishes of the rivers and the sea. Some of the source materials of this legend were provided by Ulric Williams of Wellington, N.Z.

THE IGUANA'S POISON BAG (*Australia*): Rewritten from "The Iguana and the Black Snake" in *Australian Legendary Tales*, originally collected by K. Langloh Parker, selected and edited by H. Drake-Brockman, Angus & Robertson, Ltd., Sydney, 1953. This, like many other Australian aboriginal folk tales, explains the origin of a natural phenomenon. The black snake, behaving like a trickster hero, outtalks the iguana and gets the poison which he has possessed ever since. The story also explains aboriginal observation that the iguana is one of the few animals (if not the only creature) immune to the black snake's bite.

THE TURTLE AND THE MONKEY SHARE A TREE (*The Philippines*): Based on a tale recorded in *Tagalog Texts*, by Leonard Bloomfield, University of Illinois Press, Urbana, Ill., 1917. Most of the familiar folk tales of the Philippines are of Spanish derivation, but, as in South America, there is a strong and vigorous survival of indigenous folklore. While this tale is non-European in origin, it has a theme with a familiar ring—the turtle's request that, whatever else his captor may have in mind, he be spared from the water. It recalls the New World Brer Rabbit pleading not to be thrown into the briar patch and the Ethiopian hawk pleading not to be thrown over the side of a mountain.

KANTCHIL'S LIME PIT (*Indonesia*): From *Kantchil's Lime Pit and Other Stories from Indonesia*, by Harold Courlander, Harcourt, Brace and Company, Inc., New York, 1950. The mouse deer, known variously among Indonesians as *kantchil* and the *pelandok*, is Indonesia's trickster hero. His adventures are a series of successful contests of wits with tigers, crocodiles, elephants, and other powerful creatures of the countryside. His place in Indonesian folklore parallels that of the hare, rabbit, and spider in other parts of the world.

WHY THE PARROT REPEATS MAN'S WORDS (*Thailand*): A synthesis of two variants, the first taken orally, the second in *Laos Folk-Lore of Farther India*, by K. N. Fleeson, Revell and Co., 1899. This tale explains why the parrot or parakeet is domesticated, and why his jungle cousin, the small lorikeet, is not. It is also a wry comment on a miscarriage of justice.

THE PRIEST AND THE PEAR TREE (*China*): From *Strange Stories from a Chinese Studio*, by Herbert A. Giles, Thomas De La Rue and Co., 1880. Also included in another volume by Giles, *Chinese Fairy Tales*, published by Gowans and Gray.

THE FOUR YOUNG MEN (*Burma*): From *Burmese Folk-Tales*, by Maung Htin Aung, Oxford University Press, Bombay, 1948. This tale is a combination of "impossible" stories and the insoluble dilemma. Burmese lore, though related in many ways to the lore of other areas of the Southeast and South Asia, has a distinctive flavor, marked by humor. There are many animal tales among the Burmese, and the trickster hero is the hare, who has adventures which sometimes parallel those of the *kantchil* of Indonesia. There are many heroic and epic legends also. Variants of this tale are known elsewhere in Asia, and one version is found among the Ashanti of Gold Coast. (See "The Liars' Contest" in *The Hat-Shaking Dance*, by Harold Courlander, Harcourt, Brace and Co., Inc., New York, 1956.)

THE VALIANT POTTER (*India*): An old Indian tale, distinguished by its humor and satire. The theme of the hero-by-accident and warrior-in-spite-of-himself is familiar in the Middle East and Northeast Africa. There is a Somali tale in which an unnerved warrior stalls for time while the battle rages, thinking of all sorts of excuses as he sits on his horse in front of his house, and then shouts violent challenges at the enemy as he lets his horse wander afield from the battleground. (See "The Battle of Eghal Shillet" and "The Hero of Adi Nifas" in Courlander and Leslau, *The Fire on the Mountain and Other Ethiopian Stories*, Henry Holt and Company, Inc., New York, 1950.) This rendition of "The Valiant Potter" is rewritten from Tara Sirkar's *Indian Tales Re-Told*, General Printers and Publishers, Ltd., Calcutta, 1951. Another variant is found in Mary Frere's *Old Deccan Days*.

FOUR RIDDLES (*Pakistan*): This tale is a synthesis of two variants. In one of the variants, the man who answers the riddles is a king whose four sons have been turned into stone. The variant on which this treatment is based, heard in Karachi, has as its hero a humble workman, but the actual riddles are taken from a version which appears in *Folk Tales of Kashmir*, by J. Hinton Knowles, published by Kegan Paul, Trench, Trubner & Co., London, 1893, under the title "Four Princes Turned into Stone."

THE SILVER ON THE HEARTH (*Afghanistan*): From "Some Current Pushtu Folk Stories," by F. H. Malyon, in *Memoirs of the Royal Asiatic Society of Bengal*, Vol. III, 1914. This tale is a "story within a story," extracted from a long narrative called "A Modern Story of Tirah." The familiar theme of the woman who can't keep a secret—popular in much of the old lore of Asia and Europe—here has a somewhat unusual denouement.

THE QUIVERING NEEDLE (*Iran*): From *Once the Mullah*, by Alice Geer Kelsey, Longmans, Green & Co. Inc., New York, 1954. The Mullah Nasr-ed-Din is the Iranian equivalent of Nasr-ed-Din Hodja of Turkey. The Mullah (meaning teacher or priest) is both wise and foolish. In his foolish acts, there is often hidden wisdom and humor, as in this tale; and whatever the situation, the Mullah usually manages to carry himself off with dignity. In another tale in the source book, people think he is getting old and infirm. To prove that he has not lost vitality since he was a youth, the Mullah tells a story about a large rock that he used to try to move when he was a child and a young man. He would go out periodically to test his strength on the rock, but he was never able to move it. But only recently, the Mullah tells his audience, he went back to his birthplace, where he saw the same old rock. "I stooped and took hold of it with both my hands— old man that I am. . . . And I cannot move the rock even now." See for comparison "The Hodja Preaches a Sermon" (Turkey).

THE STORK CALIPH (*Iraq*): Condensed from a story in *Tales of the Crescent Moon*, by May McNeer and Charlotte Lederer, Rinehart & Company, Inc., New York, 1930, by permission of authors and publishers. This is a story of old Bagdad of the Arabian Nights era, which ended about the middle of the thirteenth century.

IMPOSSIBLE TALES (*Syria*): This story is a synthesis of two overlapping variants, one heretofore unpublished, the other recounted under the title "The Story That Is All Lies" in Habib Katibah's *Other Arabian Nights*, Charles Scribner's Sons, New York, 1929. In the Katibah version, the storyteller is none other than Abu Nuwas, the poet-entertainer of Harun-al-Rashid's court, who figures in the Saudi Arabian tale in this collection, "Abunuwas, the Wit." As indicated elsewhere, Abu Nuwas tales are known and told throughout the Middle East, in Arab-influenced cultures in North and East Africa, and even as far away as Indonesia.

THE HODJA PREACHES A SERMON (*Turkey*): From *Tales From Turkey*, by Allan Ramsay and Francis McCullagh, Simpkin, Marshall, Hamilton, Kent and Co., 1914. This wit and humor is characteristic of many tales from Turkey and other regions influenced by Islamic lore. (See "The Quivering Needle" and "The Tail of St. George's Dragon" in this collection.) In North Africa this incident is sometimes heard as part of the Abu Nuwas cycle. In another part of the world, the United States, it shows up as an "Afro-American" folk tale.

ABUNUWAS, THE WIT (*Saudi Arabia*): From *Abu Nuwas in Life and Legend*, by W. H. Ingrams, privately printed at Port Louis, Mauritius, 1933. Abunuwas (also spelled Abu Nuwas and

286

Abunawas) was in real life a poet in the time of Harun-al-Rashid, and he was well known to Harun, being a member of the courtly circle. A vast number of apocryphal tales have grown up around Abunuwas, unrelated to the facts of his life. In the course of time, Abunuwas has become a trickster hero to Arabic-speaking people in Iraq, Arabia, and North Africa. Many Somali and Libyan tales are told about him—adventures in which he outwits kings, merchants, and farmers. Many of the tales are risqué, inspired no doubt by the reputation earned by the poet prototype. In numerous tales, Abunuwas is cast in the role filled by traditional tricksters in other cultures. The episodes recounted here are typical, but represent only a fleeting taste of the seemingly endless Abunuwas repertoire. The incident of stealing the odors of the meat and repayment by the tinkle of money is known in modern Mexico with a typical Mexican setting.

THE TAIL OF ST. GEORGE'S DRAGON (*Lebanon*): From *Arabian Romances and Folk Tales*, by Habib T. Katibah, Charles Scribner's Sons, New York, 1929.

THE HORSE WITHOUT A MASTER (*Yemen*): From *Wonder Tales of Horses and Heroes*, by Frances Carpenter, Doubleday & Company, Inc., New York, 1952.

DON'T THROW STONES FROM NOT YOURS TO YOURS (*Israel*): An oral version of an ancient tale, narrated by Joseph Meltzer. Originally from the *Babylonian Talmud Baba Kama* and *Tosefta Baba Kama*, Chapter II.

THE JUDGMENT OF KARAKOUSH (*Egypt*): From *Arabian Romances and Folk Tales*, by Habib T. Katibah, Charles Scribner's Sons, New York, 1929. Karakoush (whose full name was Baha-ud-Din Ibn Abdullah al-Asdi Karakoush) was a freed slave of Saladin, Sultan of Egypt and Syria during the last part of the twelfth century. Saladin made Karakoush Governor of Cairo and, at another time, of Acre. This story may well be apocryphal, inasmuch as it is known elsewhere in Asia. A similar story is told in Ceylon, where it is known as "The Trial at Avichára-Pura." In Ceylon too the tale is used as the basis of a proverb: "Like the trial at Avichára-Pura."

THE FIRE ON THE MOUNTAIN (*Ethiopia*): From *The Fire on the Mountain and Other Ethiopian Stories*, by Harold Courlander and Wolf Leslau, Henry Holt and Company, Inc., New York, 1950, reprinted by permission of the publishers. This tale, which is known in many forms on virtually every continent, recalls the incident in "Abunuwas, the Wit" in which odors are paid for by the tinkle of money. The theme of this Ethiopian variant, however, is contemplative in nature and stresses the value of the spirit of the law over the letter of the law.

THE GHOST-BIRD (*Union of South Africa*): From *Tales from the Kraals*, by Madeline Murgatroyd, Central News Agency, Ltd., 1944. This story, a rewriting of a Zulu legend, explains why the tickbird is often seen on the backs of cattle and other grazing animals. The lore of the Zulu and related peoples is full of explanations of natural phenomena and how certain things came to be. There is often an air of poetic wonder about things in nature, and elaborate stories are told to account for them. Among the tales of South Africa there are, of course, many of European origin and inspiration as well.

HOW PAKAYANA THE SPIDER GOT HIS SMALL WAIST (*Liberia*): From a version collected by Ellen M. Moore, Kakata, Liberia. Pakayana the spider is the trickster hero in the folklore of Liberia. In fact, the spider plays the trickster role in a wide area of West Africa, being known among the Ashanti of Gold Coast and elsewhere as Anansi. Pakayana (or Anansi) is a curious combination of cleverness, wit, foolishness, and greed. In contests with the large and strong animals he often emerges the victor. His shrewdness often amazes the other creatures of the forest. And yet he is habitually victimized by his own acts of avarice and stupidity. The spider trickster has survived in the New World with little change in his character. In many of the islands of the West Indies, in British Guiana, and in southern United States he is known under his Ashanti name, being called, variously, Anansi, Brer 'Nansi, Sister Nancy, etc.

THE SON OF THE HUNTER (*Greece*): Rewritten from a tale in *Modern Greek Folk Tales*, by R. M. Dawkins, Oxford University Press, London, 1953, by permission of The Clarendon Press, Oxford, England. This appears to be an ancient tale in the pattern of the powerful or magic companions who assist the hero to accomplish seemingly impossible deeds. The theme of tests or ordeals is widespread in European and Asian lore. In the present Greek variant there appears to be mention of an athletic feat of a bygone day—jumping with the aid of stones. According to the collector of the tale, the stones are hurled backwards to aid the jumper in his forward leap.

KING SVATOPLUK AND THE THREE STICKS (*Czechoslovakia*): The theme of being able to break sticks singly but not when they are bound together appears frequently in Western folklore. In some tales the idea is reversed to show that a person may not be able to do a great deed all at once, but if he proceeds slowly (one stick at a time) he will eventually be able to accomplish his objective. Thus the parable of the sticks is used to project different ideas. The theme here, obviously, is that "In unity there is strength." This concept of the bound sticks was known in ancient Rome, where a bundle of bound rods with a projecting ax blade was the badge of authority of the magistrates. The symbol appears on United States dimes with the motto: *E Pluribus Unum.*

THE BEST WISH (*Yugoslavia*): From *Legends of the United Nations*, by Frances Frost, Whittlesey House, McGraw-Hill Book Company, Inc., New York, 1946.

THE OLD FATHER WHO WENT TO SCHOOL (*Ukrainian S.S.R.*): From *Cossack Fairy Tales and Folk Tales*, by R. Nisbet Bain, Lawrence and Bullen, 1894. In this tale one may detect the folk version of the King Lear theme, with sons rather than daughters acting as the ungrateful children. Other elements of the King Lear theme are to be found in the Swedish tale, "Salt and Bread."

THE KING AND THE PEASANT (*Poland*): From *Polish Folk Tales*, translated by Lucia Merecka Borski, Sheed & Ward, Inc., New York, 1947. The translator notes: "The king referred to in this story is most probably King Kazimir the Great, who merited the title 'The King of the Peasants' for his considerate treatment of them."

THE SOLDIER AND THE KNAPSACK (*Byelorussia*): This tale of the magic knapsack and of the man who stays death's hand and who cannot get into heaven or hell is known widely in Eastern Europe, and a New World variant is told in Mexico. The theme of the man who is feared by the devils, and who is sent away from the gates of hell, appears in a number of Negro tales in the United States and the West Indies.

THE SNAKE AND THE DREAMS (*Union of Soviet Socialist Republics*): Rewritten from "The Serpent and the Peasant" in *Georgian Folk Tales*, by M. Wardrop, David Nutt, 1894.

THE CONTRARY WIFE (*Norway*): A traditional Norwegian tale retold. A similar story is known in Ethiopia and elsewhere in the Middle East.

SALT AND BREAD (*Sweden*): An old Swedish tale, retold. This story is widespread through Europe in many forms. Often the "salt and bread" motif is essential to the plot, but there are numerous similar tales which develop other action around jealousy of a sister. One might compare this story with "King Lear," "Cinderella," and the old English ballad "The Three Sisters."

THE TALISMAN (*Denmark*): By Hans Christian Andersen. From *The Complete Andersen*, Vol. 3, translated by Jean Hersholt, Limited Editions Club, George Macy Companies, Incorporated, New York, 1942 and 1949. By the kind permission of the translator.

THE FIDDLER OF ECHTERNACH (*Luxembourg*): From *Luxembourg, Land of Legends*, by W. J. Taylor-Whitehead, Constable & Co., Ltd., London, 1951. The tale of the magic fiddle (or drum or flute) which makes people dance against their will is among the most universal folklore themes, being known in Europe, Asia, Africa, and the Americas. Here, however, it is tied to a legendary event and, moreover, to the uncontrollable movements associated with St. Vitus's (i.e., Viet's) dance.

THE BRIDGE OF ST. CLOUD (*France*): Translated from a story in *Légendaire des Provinces Françaises* by R. Devigne, Horizons de France, Paris. The theme of outwitting Satan at his own game is a favorite one in European lore. In some tales the Devil bargains for a child in the family and is outwitted by a similar ruse. One Anglo-American comic ballad tells how the devil gets a farmer's wife through such a compact, but she is such a shrew that he can't stand her and begs the farmer to take her away.

THE LADY OF STAVOREN (*The Netherlands*): A legend from the Province of Friesland, from *Tales Told in Holland*, Book House for Children, Chicago, 1926. Used by permission of the author, Olive Beaupré Miller, and the publishers.

THE SOUP STONE (*Belgium*): Reprinted by permission from *The Soup Stone* by Maria Leach, Funk & Wagnalls Company, New York, 1954.

KING JOHN AND THE ABBOT OF CANTERBURY (*Great Britain*): Based on an old English ballad included in Bishop Percy's Reliques (1729–1811), this legend, known elsewhere in Europe, has here been identified with historical characters. One of the riddles or questions put to the Abbot is certainly of English invention—the one relating to King John's worth. The clever reply is based, of course, on a pun on the word sovereign—meaning as well as king, a gold coin worth twenty shillings.

BUKOLLA (*Iceland*): Another widespread folklore theme—the chase and the magic objects thrown on the ground which turn into obstacles for the pursuer. Variants are known in Europe, Asia, and Africa. In the African versions the magic objects are frequently eggs.

THE DEER AND THE JAGUAR SHARE A HOUSE (*Brazil*): From a manuscript in the New York Public Library, collector unknown. Here we have a universally comic situation in which the protagonists are equally mystified and chagrined by the circumstances. This Indian tale attempts to explain why the jaguar and the deer do not live together. It also makes the moral observation that a creature is revolted by the thought of eating its own kind.

KAKUÍ, BIRD OF THE NIGHT (*Argentina*): A legend widely known in Argentina.

THE COMING OF ASIN (*Bolivia*): Based on Indian legends in *Myths of the Toba and Pilagá Indians of the Gran Chaco*, by Alfred Métraux, American Folk-Lore Society Memoirs, No. 40, 1946. This legend is about a culture hero of the Gran Chaco region. Asin is, of course, a powerful magician. The fox-skin cloak which he wears (in some variants a donkey skin) is a magical one. From under this cloak he is able to bring out food and other needs as he desires. In this fragment of the Asin legend, we have a tale which begins in a familiar pattern—the poor and ugly man who is despised as a beggar, but who is really intelligent and handsome in his metamorphic form. As in certain oriental tales, he is not quick to reveal his noble qualities and does so only after he has given others an opportunity to show their generosity or their cruel attitudes. After the great battle in which Asin, single-handed, defeats the enemy, the tale takes on an epic quality, with Asin wreaking revenge on his enemies. In some of the Indian tales Asin is credited with bringing fire to man; other tales give the credit to other culture heroes. But in this variant, at least, Asin monopolizes fire when it is most needed, and thus destroys those who had treated him badly. It is not clear whether Asin causes the storm and cold, or whether he simply has foresight of its arrival. The annihilation of the population in this disaster, and the preservation of the friends of Asin, recalls the deluge myths of many other peoples, including the Biblical story of Noah.

THE LEGEND OF THE CHINGOLO BIRD (*Paraguay*): Translated and rewritten from a tale recorded in Spanish by María Concepción de Chaves.

THE ORIGIN OF THE CAMLET FLOWER (*Uruguay*): Retold from *Poesias y Leyendas Para los Ninos*, by Fernan Silva Valdes, published by A. Monteverde y Cia, Montevideo.

THE FIVE EGGS (*Ecuador*): Reprinted from *Stories from the Americas*, collected and translated by Frank Henius, Charles Scribner's Sons, New York, 1944, used by permission of the publishers. This tale appears to be European in origin. The theme of playing dead as an act of stubbornness, to the edge of the grave itself, is frequent in European lore.

THE MAGIC SANDALS OF HUALACHI (*Peru*): From *Cuentos de Hadas de la America del Sur*, by Pilo Mayo, Editorial Molino, Buenos Aires, 1943. The appearance of the legend of magic sandals among the Incas is very interesting. In their essential attributes, these sandals do not differ much from those of the Greek god Hermes. In less ancient European lore there is a wide variety of magical shoes, such as the "Seven League Boots." As for the roads and highways along which the Peruvian *chasquis* ran with their messages, many of them, with the ruins of the rest houses, may still be seen.

HOW LIFE AND LIGHT CAME INTO THE WORLD (*Colombia*): This fragment of Chibcha Indian creation mythology has a special poetic quality. The making of humans and other creatures out of primeval mud has parallels on every continent. Indonesians and Indians of the United States share a myth that the Creator made three tries at producing human beings shaped out of earth. On the first try he places the figures over the fire to cook, but they weren't done enough; on the second try they were overcooked and too dark; but on the third try they were cooked just right, and the brown man came into being. The results of the first two tries, according to Indonesian and U.S. Indian (Washo) lore, were the white and negro races. This tale is based on a manuscript provided by the Ministry of Education, Bogotá, Colombia.

THE SINGING FLUTE (*Venezuela*): From *Datos sobre el Folklore de la Región de El Tocuyo*, by Francisco Tamayo. Extract from *Monografía de El Tocuyo*, Caracas, 1945.

THE GOLDEN ALTAR OF THE CHURCH OF ST. JOSEPH (*Panama*): An old Panamanian legend retold by Delia Arias, Cultural Attaché, Delegation of Panama to the United Nations.

UNCLE COYOTE'S LAST MISCHIEF (*Nicaragua*): From an unpublished manuscript by Orlando Cuadra Downing, by kind permission of the author. Coyote is the hero and buffoon of many peoples throughout Central America. See "Señor Coyote and the Dogs."

THE PEASANT AND THE HORSEMAN (*Costa Rica*):
Translated and adapted from "The Indian and the Spaniard" in
Cuentos Viejos (*Old Tales*) by María de Noguera, Lehmann &
Co., Costa Rica, 1952.

THE ORIGIN OF THE BALSAM TREE (*El Salvador*):
Translated and adapted from the Spanish of Salvador Salazar
Arrué (Salarrué), with the permission of the author.

THE FALL OF THE EARTH GIANTS (*Honduras*): This is
a creation myth of the Maya-Quiche people, who lived in Honduras, Guatemala, and El Salvador at the time of the Spanish
Conquest. These people were a branch of the widespread Maya
culture, and the Quiche language is still spoken in Central America
today. Myths of the ancient Maya were recorded in a book called
Popul Vuh (Collection of Written Leaves) by Mayan scholars in
the Quiche language. The book, generally believed to have been
compiled in the seventeenth century, was lost for many years and
rediscovered only in 1854 in the University of San Carlos in Guatemala. Some of the substance of this Mayan literature was repro-
duced in English by Lewis Spence in his *Myths of Mexico and
Peru*, Thomas Y. Crowell Company, New York, 1913, and the episodes appearing here were taken from that book by permission of
George G. Harrap & Co., Ltd., London. (The entire *Popol Vuh*
has recently been translated and published in English.) In the
myth of the earth giants there seems to be much symbolism. The
two sons of Vukub-Cakix—Cabrakan and Zipacna—are obviously
the forces of the earthquake and the volcano. Vukub-Cakix himself is portrayed as the Great Macaw, and Spence speaks of him
as the sun-god and sometimes the earth. This latter interpretation has special meaning in connection with the placing of white
maize in his mouth when his teeth are removed. The god Hurakan, the mighty wind, appears to be the origin of our own word
hurricane. (Some authorities give the origin as Taino, Indians
of the West Indies who came from the mainland.) In myths of
this kind there is no implicit moral point, no particular sense of
justice or right or wrong. In the days of the creation, the gods
and other creatures were locked in a struggle for control of the
world. As far as the evidence goes, the earth giants did nothing
to warrant their fate. The gods simply wished to be rid of them
because the earth giants did not respect their rule.

THE EMERALD LIZARD (*Guatemala*): From the Spanish of
Carlos Samayoa Chinchilla, by permission of the author. This is
one of the countless miracle-type legends which abound in the
lore of Central and South America. (See "The Golden Altar of
the Church of St. Joseph.") Pedro de San Joseph de Bethancourt, who figures in the story, was born in Chafna, Villaflor de
Teneriffe, in the Canary Islands on March 19, 1626. His father,
Amador González de la Rosa Bethancourt, was descended from a
Norman noble named Jean de Bethancourt, upon whom King
John II bestowed the governorship of the Canary Islands as a reward for having won these islands for his country. Arriving in
Guatemala from Spain in 1651, Pedro joined the order of St. Francis, entering the priesthood in 1656. He founded a hospice for
pilgrims and the homeless and also a primary school for Indian
children. Later he founded the Order of Bethlehem and a hos-
pital for the sick. At the beginning of his charitable work, his
only helpers were an old woman and a deaf mute. He died on
April 25, 1667, venerated by many people. His tomb may be seen
in the chapel of the Church of St. Francis in Santiago, Guatemala.

SEÑOR COYOTE AND THE DOGS (*Mexico*): From *Picture Tales from Mexico*, by Dan Storm. Reprinted by permission
of the publisher, J. B. Lippincott Company, Philadelphia, 1941.
Coyote is a trickster figure from the old lore of many Indian peoples
of North America. Like tricksters in many other cultures, the
coyote is known for his capacity to perform utterly silly acts, as
in this tale.

THE BEEF TONGUE OF ORULA (*Cuba*): From *Cuentos
y Leyendas Negras de Cuba*, by Ramón Guirao, Ediciones "Mira-
dor" Colección "Verso y Prosa," Havana. This tale appears to
be a very old one, of Yoruba origin, explaining how the Yoruba
deity, Orula, came by his title "Ruler of the World." Yoruba
traditions and lore have been kept alive in Cuba in the Lucumí
cult, which possesses a pantheon of deities, each identified with
some special quality or natural force. Both Orula and Obatalá
are of Yoruba beginnings.

UNCLE BOUKI RENTS A HORSE (*Haiti*): From *Uncle
Bouqui of Haiti* by Harold Courlander, William Morrow & Com-

pany, New York, 1942. Nonc' Bouki is one of the traditional characters of Haitian folklore. He often appears in combination with Ti Malice, who is his constant nemesis, as in this story. Many of the Bouki-Malice tales appear to be old Anansi stories (see notes on "How Pakayana the Spider Got His Small Waist") adapted to locally invented protoganists.

THE KING'S TOWER (*Dominican Republic*): From *Folklore of the Dominican Republic*, by Manuel de Andrade, American Folklore Society, 1930.

PAUL BUNYAN'S CORNSTALK (*United States*): Paul Bunyan is the hero of a vast number of tales set in the background of the lumbering camps of the United States. No one knows for sure whether the stories about Paul Bunyan began as true folklore or as literary invention, but the well-known folklorist Stith Thompson states that he heard the Paul Bunyan yarns in the Oregon woods a good while before they were popularized in print. In any case, the tall tales about this Gargantuan hero were known in many a lumbering camp from Maine to Michigan, and from Wisconsin to the Pacific Coast. The nature of the colossal exaggeration in the Bunyan tales has been very inviting to the storytellers of the lumber camps and the writer alike; it is the kind of humor which precipitates spontaneous invention of new episodes and wider fancy. The incidents from Paul Bunyan's career included here were recorded by Harold Courlander in rural Michigan. In some variants, Paul Bunyan kills the cornstalk by wrapping a steel rail from an abandoned railroad around it so that it chokes itself as it grows.

JEAN LABADIE'S DOG (*Canada*): Adapted from "Jean Labadie's Big Black Dog" from *The Talking Cat* by Natalie Savage Carlson, Harper & Brothers, New York, 1952.

THE TOROMIRO OF RAPA-NUI (*Chile*): Adapted from a tale in *Tradiciones de la Isla Pascua* by P. Sebastian Englert, Publicaciones de la Comision de Estudios sobre la Isla Pascua, Universidad de Chile, 1939. Easter Island is the easternmost island of Polynesia in the Pacific. This legend attempts to explain the origin of certain wood carvings allegedly still found there. The tale is, of course, Polynesian rather than European or from the New World.